CW00666120

CLOCK CLEANING AND REPAIRING

CLOCK CLEANING
AND REPAIRING

Edited by

Bernard E. Jones

With 94 Illustrations

CASSELL · LONDON

CASSELL & COMPANY LTD

an imprint of
Cassell & Collier Macmillan Publishers Ltd
35 Red Lion Square, London WC1R 4SG
and at Sydney, Auckland, Toronto, Johannesburg

and an affiliate of The Macmillan Company Inc, New York

First edition 1917
Second edition, completely revised, February 1954
Third edition February 1957
Fourth edition May 1964
Fifth edition November 1965
Sixth edition April 1967
Sixth edition, second impression October 1968
Sixth edition, third impression April 1970
Sixth edition, fifth impression December 1974
Sixth edition, sixth impression October 1976

ISBN 0 304 91801 6

Printed in Great Britain by Fletcher & Son Ltd, Norwich
and bound by Richard Clay (The Chaucer Press) Ltd,
Bungay, Suffolk

974

EDITOR'S PREFACE

THIS practical handbook on the cleaning and repairing of domestic clocks is largely the work of a practical horologist who prefers to hide his identity under the initial "G". In it, he gives the results of a lifetime of experience in the clock making and repairing industry. Writing with authority, he is yet able to put his instructions into such a clear and simple form that every reader should be able to understand them.

The book has a wide scope, and covers most of the work likely to be met with in normal clock repair work. In this latest edition, it has been revised and added to in order to bring it right up to date.

B. E. J.

ACKNOWLEDGMENTS

The Editor wishes to thank the following firms for much valuable technical assistance, and for permission to use examples of their products for illustrations:—

Messrs. Smith's English Clocks, Ltd., of Cricklewood.
Messrs. F. W. Elliott, Ltd., of Croydon.
Messrs. Gent & Co., Ltd., of Leicester.
Messrs. Gillett & Johnston, Ltd., of Croydon.
Messrs. Robert Pringle & Sons, of Clerkenwell.
Messrs. H. & R. Elliott, of Croydon.
Messrs. James Neill & Co. (Sheffield), Ltd., of Sheffield.
The Synchronome Company, Ltd., of Alperton.
The Bentima Company, Ltd., of London.
Ferranti, Ltd., of Manchester.
Mettamec, Ltd., of East Dereham.
English Clock Systems, Ltd., of London.

Thanks are also due to two enthusiastic horologists for their kindness and help. They are:—

Walter H. Bentley, Esq., F.B.H.I., and
Francis E. Fryer, Esq., M.B.H.I.

CONTENTS

CHAPTER 1

How a Simple Clock Works

A **Spring-driven Pendulum Clock.**—It is customary to regard the mechanism of a clock as something that is either mysterious or remarkably complicated. As a matter of fact, the ordinary domestic clock is neither.

A typical example of a simple eight-day spring-driven "timepiece" (that is, a clock which only *indicates time*, and does not *strike*), is illustrated in Figs. 1 and 2. Its frame consists of two brass plates, spaced and united by four pillars. In the frame is mounted the "train", a series of wheels and pinions, by which the power of the mainspring is transmitted in stages to the hands, and to the "escapement", the device by which the power of the spring is controlled so that its speed of release can be governed by the pendulum.

The spring is enclosed in a cylindrical casing, called the "going barrel", on one end of which is mounted the first or "main" wheel of the train. One end of the mainspring is attached to the inner side of the wall of the barrel, and the opposite end of the spring is hooked on to the central spindle, which is known as the "barrel arbor". This arbor is rotated by the key when the clock is wound, and, as it is prevented from moving backwards by a ratchet mechanism, power is stored in the mainspring.

This power causes the main wheel, and through it the rest of the train, to rotate at a speed governed by the pendulum. To enable this to be done, the final wheel of the train has specially shaped teeth, and is called the "escape wheel". Its special teeth engage in turn with a pair of shaped steel blocks, called "pallets", which permit the teeth to pass them in a kind of step-by-step manner

7

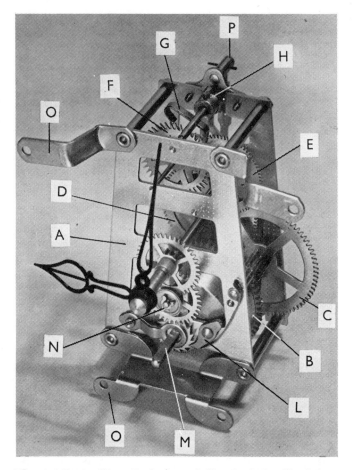

Fig. 1.—Front Plate End-view of Simple 8-day Pendulum Timepiece. Made by Smith's English Clocks Ltd.

A—Frame Plates; B—Main Wheel and Going Barrel; C—Intermediate Wheel; D—Centre Wheel; E—Third Wheel; F—Escape Wheel; G—Pallets; H—Crutch; L—Winding Click, or Pawl; M—Winding Square and Ratchet; N—Motion-work Wheels and Pinions; O—Fixing Lugs (for case mounting); P—Suspension Pillar.

Fig. 2.—Back Plate View of Simple 8-day Pendulum Time-piece. Made by Smith's English Clocks Ltd.

A—Frame Plates; B—Main Wheel and Going Barrel; C—Intermediate Wheel; E—Third Wheel; G—Pallets; H—Crutch; J—Pendulum Rod; K—Pendulum Bob; N—Motion-work Wheels and Pinions; O—Fixing Lugs; P—Suspension Pillar.

as the pendulum swings. These pallets are linked to the pendulum by a "crutch", a bar attached to one end of the pallet spindle, and shaped at the other end to engage with the pendulum rod.

The third wheel and pinion of the train are usually so arranged that they make one turn each hour, and the minute hand of the clock is mounted on the front end of the suitably lengthened spindle of this wheel and pinion. The hour hand is driven at one-twelfth of the minute hand speed by means of a special set of wheels and pinions, known as the "motion-work", which has a 12 to 1 ratio between its first pinion, mounted on the minute hand, and its final wheel, known as the "hour wheel". The hour wheel is mounted on a tube, called a "pipe", which rides on the minute hand spindle. The hour hand is fitted to this pipe, and so, by this means, both hour and minute hands are arranged to rotate concentrically, but at the required different speeds.

A simple form of slipping clutch is always fitted to the minute hand spindle to enable the hands to be set to time when necessary without any interference with the main wheelwork of the clock. The tension of the clutch spring is set so as to provide enough grip for the hands to be driven correctly in all normal circumstances, but to permit them to be moved by the slight extra force applied when the setting is done.

An examination of the illustrations of the simple "Smith" timepiece shown in Figs. 1 and 2 will make the position and action of all these parts quite clear. This particular clock has been chosen because it enables all the essential parts of an ordinary domestic timepiece to be seen, and their action understood.

The Escapement.—This is the most important part of a clock, for its function is a dual one. It has the double duty of relating the movements of the wheels and pinions of the train to the steady, even measurement of time intervals carried out by the pendulum, and transmitting to the pendulum some of the energy supplied by the main-spring, in order to keep the pendulum swinging continuously. To put it another way, the escapement has to allow the wheelwork to move forward in regular steps when the swing of the pendulum permits, and to give the pendulum small "doses" of energy to make good the losses due to air-friction and similar things that would eventually bring it to a stop.

If a repairer is to adjust or repair an escapement correctly, it is essential for him to understand its action. This is where many amateurs fail. They are quite capable of cleaning clocks and assembling them, but they often fail to detect escapement faults which they would soon discover if they had a more complete knowledge of correct escapement action. This often renders much of their other work of little value, and leads to many disappointments. For this reason, a little time spent in acquiring an understanding of escapements is well repaid.

All pendulum controlled escapements consist of an escape wheel and a pair of pallets. The teeth of the escape wheel are of special form, and the pallets are small blocks of steel, so mounted and pivoted that as one advances and engages with a tooth on the escape wheel, the other recedes for a corresponding distance and disengages with the tooth with which it has been in contact. The relative spacing of the two pallets in relation to the escape wheel teeth is arranged so that when one tooth is resting on one pallet, the other pallet will be midway between two other teeth. By this means, the teeth of the escape wheel are permitted to move forward, step-by-step, a distance equal to half the space between two teeth at each engagement and disengagement of the pallets and wheel teeth. The movement of the pallets is, of course, controlled by the swing of the pendulum, and by this action, the speed of rotation of the escape wheel is governed.

In addition to engaging with the teeth of the escape wheel, and so controlling the time of their step-by-step release, the pallets also serve to transmit to the pendulum the small pulses of energy, known as "impulses", which maintain its swing. For this purpose, the acting faces of the pallets are formed as inclined planes, on which the teeth of the escape wheel exert a slight thrust as they pass. The amount of this thrust is designed to be as nearly as possible equal to the energy lost by the pendulum, and this maintains the constant swing of the pendulum, and so keeps the clock going.

As it is not possible for one pallet to come into action at exactly the point where the other ceases to act, a small amount of free forward motion of the escape wheel is permitted at each movement of the pallets. This ensures the correct action of the escapement, and is known as the "drop".

The most usual escapement for a domestic clock is the "recoil" (Fig. 31), so called because the slight continued swing of the pendulum after a tooth of the escape wheel has engaged with a pallet causes the escape wheel to move backwards slightly, or "recoil". This escapement is a simple and reliable one, and if in good condition it can perform very well.

A somewhat different form, also used on domestic clocks, is known as the "dead-beat". It is shown in Fig. 38. In this escapement, the escape wheel teeth, which differ slightly from those of the recoil, fall upon parts of the pallets which are shaped to be portions of the arcs of circles struck from the pivot point of the pallets. During this portion of the action, the tooth which is resting on the pallet does not move forward or back, but as the swing of the pallets continues, the tooth moves from the curved surface of the pallet, which is known as the "dead" or "locking" face, to the inclined, or "impulse" face, and so delivers its impulse to the pallet. The action of a dead-beat escapement is more precise than that of a recoil, and it is used on the more accurate types of clocks.

A Weight-driven Pendulum Clock.—This is much the same as the spring-driven clock, but the driving force is supplied by a weight, which is suspended from either a line or a chain. If a line is used, one end of it is attached to a drum, or "barrel", and the rest of the line is then coiled around the barrel during the winding operation. If the weight is hung from a chain, the barrel is replaced by a sprocket wheel, which engages with the links of the chain, and so transmits the drive.

In either case, the barrel or sprocket is linked to the main wheel by a ratchet mechanism, which enables the weight to be wound up when the going of the clock has allowed it to descend.

In all other ways, the weight-driven clock is similar to the spring-driven form. The real advantage of the weight drive is that it exerts an even amount of power on the wheel-work at all times, a feature that cannot be obtained with even the best mainspring. Mainsprings pull more powerfully when fully wound than they do when nearly run down, but the power of a weight is practically unvarying.

The disadvantage of the weight-driven clock is that it requires much more space than a spring-driven one, for adequate space for the weight fall must be provided.

A Spring-driven Balance Clock.—Neither of the clocks so far described is truly portable. Moving them means a temporary interference with their time-keeping function. The commonest portable clock is, to all intents and purposes, a large edition of a watch (see Fig. 3). Instead of a pendulum, it has a balance (see Fig. 4), which is in effect a flywheel mounted on pivots so as to spin quite freely. On the same spindle as the balance is a hair-spring which causes the balance, when given an impulse, to vibrate backwards and forwards in a certain definite interval of time, the duration of which depends on the weight of the balance and the tension of the hairspring. It thus acts in a similar way to a pendulum and forms a time measurer, because each vibration, whether long or short, is performed in the same time. By connecting

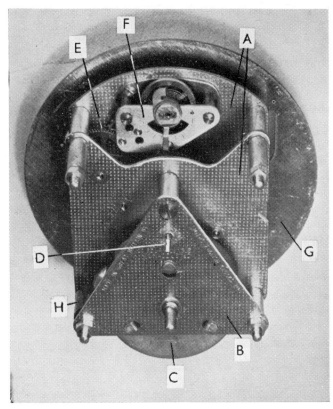

Fig. 3.—Modern 8-day Timepiece with Pin-pallet Platform Escapement. Made by Smith's English Clocks Ltd., and known as the QH. 100.

A—Frame Plates; B—Sub-Plate for Main Arbor and Mainspring Barrel; C—Mainspring Barrel (a Fixed Barrel); D—Centre Arbor; E—Fourth Wheel; F—Pin-Pallet Platform Escapement (mounted on Front Plate of Frame); G—Dial Sub-Plate.

such a balance and hairspring with a suitable escapement, that, like a pendulum escapement, will give the balance a little impulse at each beat to keep it going, and at the

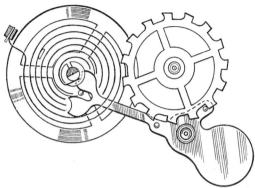

Fig. 4.—Typical Pin-pallet Lever Escapement.

same time allow one tooth to pass the pallets, a time-keeper will result which is nearly as good as a pendulum clock, and is portable, for clocks with balances may be moved or carried about in various positions without greatly affecting their accuracy. There is no crutch attached to the pallets, as in a pendulum clock. Its place is taken by a lever, at one end of which is a fork which engages with the impulse pin, and so gives impulse to the balance. The other end of the lever is enlarged merely to balance it. This escapement, which is common to all pin-pallet lever escapement clocks, is further referred to in Chapter 12.

It may be said that a watch lever escapement acts in exactly the same way as these lever-clock escapements; but the parts are more accurately and more solidly made, the impulse pin being a ruby and the lever having jewelled pallets, etc. In general, a study of these clocks will go far towards explaining the action of a lever watch.

CHAPTER 2

Clock Repairers' Tools and Materials

IT is not proposed to deal with tools and materials at length, inasmuch as the space in this book is needed for practical instruction on clock cleaning and repairing, and the workman can undertake a variety of jobs with quite a small tool outfit. The tools illustrated will be useful in different sizes for both watch and clock work. Indeed, ordinary watchmakers' tools are used, supplemented by a larger pair of pliers, a stronger screwdriver, a pair of hand tongs, and larger broaches, drills, and files. A clock lathe is larger, but otherwise similar to a watch lathe. There must be: A suitable bench or board; a "parallel" vice (Fig. 5), or, preferably, two vices, one with jaws 1 inch wide and the other with jaws $2\frac{1}{2}$ inches wide; several pairs of pliers and tweezers with jaws and points of various shapes, such as flat, half-round, round, and so on (Figs. 7 and 8); cutting nippers; a pair of sliding tongs (Fig. 9); a stout pin-vice (Fig. 9); and a strong hand vice. Several screwdrivers of various sizes are also required: a watch screwdriver (Fig. 9) for one, and another with a blade $\frac{1}{4}$ in. wide and a good strong handle. A star key or an adjustable key is a necessity. A stake and several small punches, round and flat ended, and a pillar file and a potance file will be required in addition. Also, a set of broaches for opening out holes, similar to watch broaches but larger, and some clock drills and a drill-stock (those bought ready-made answer every purpose). Some clock peg-wood and one or two fine emery sticks (emery-paper on wood) will almost complete the outfit. Those who possess a small lathe of $2\frac{1}{2}$ in. or 3 in. centre will find it very useful for drilling and turning arbors, pinions, etc.,

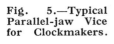

Fig. 5.—Typical Parallel-jaw Vice for Clockmakers.

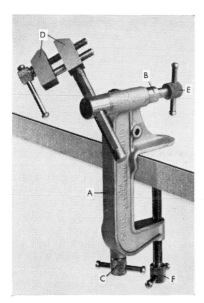

Fig. 6.—Eclipse Instrument Maker's Vice.

A—Main Frame;
B—Adjustable and Calibrated Rotatable Barrel;
C—Clamping Screw for Barrel;
D—Parallel Vice;
E—Clamping Screw for Vice;
F—Bench Attachment Clamping Screw.

B

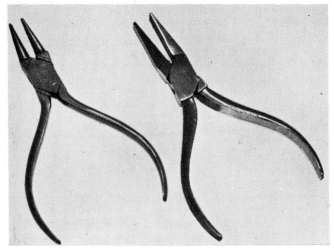

Fig. 7.—Roundnose and Flatnose Pliers.

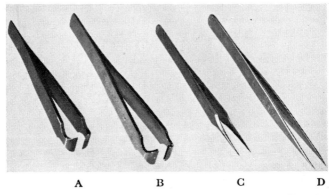

A   B   C   D

Fig. 8.—Tweezers. A and B are for hand removal, C and D
for general use.

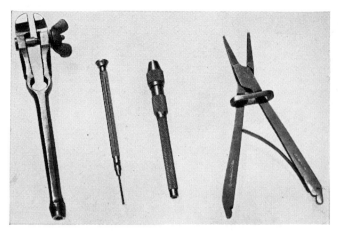

Fig. 9.—Pin-vice, Lowell Screwdriver, Pin-chuck for Hand Use and Sliding Tongs.

Fig. 10.—Round-bed Watchmaker's Lathe with Draw-in Headstock, T-rest and Tailstock. A Clockmaker's Lathe is similar, but larger.

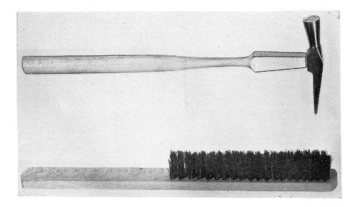

Fig. 11.—Hammer and Brush.

Fig. 12.—Eye-glass, Oil-pot and Oiler.

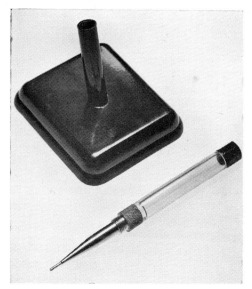

Fig. 13.—A very useful type of Oiler operating on the Hypodermic Syringe Principle.

and also for cleaning up certain parts. A special watch-maker's lathe is shown in Fig. 10. Some square gravers of assorted sizes will be needed for turning, and also a smooth stone for sharpening them.

The special hammer is shown by Fig. 11; the oiler by Fig. 12; the oil-cup by Fig. 12; the brush by Fig. 11; and the eyeglass used for watchwork and fine clockwork by Fig. 12. A special form of oiler, based on the principle of the hypodermic syringe, is made by the firm of H. & R. Elliott, of Croydon. It is excellent, for it keeps the oil clean and enables it to be placed just where it is wanted (Fig. 13).

Petrol will be required for dissolving the old oil and

grease, and there must be a bowl to put it in; rotten-stone for scouring; and a brush already illustrated (a soft clock brush) to use with it. A tin of any good metal polish is also very useful; indeed, it is almost essential. Hot water and soap are also used for removing oil, etc., but thorough drying afterwards is required, and every detachable part must be first removed, as otherwise the wet will remain and rust in all crevices. The following is good for cleansing clock plates: Boil 8 oz. of soft soap in 1 gal. of water, and when cold add 8 oz. of ammonia. Soak the plates, etc., in the solution until clean, and then brush well.

Clock oil is generally refined sperm oil, though other oils are used. The essential properties are: it should not dry up or set hard for several years, it should remain fluid at low temperatures (say to 15° below freezing), and it should not decompose or corrode the metal plates or pivots. On clocks of any value it is not advisable to use any other than the best quality clock oil. Oil drying off is a common occurrence, and is attributed to too much oil applied to the pivot holes (any oil getting over the oil sink is drawn away by capillary attraction); particles of dirt left on the pivots or in the holes; particles of rust left on the pivots; or inferior oil.

For polishing and grinding, whiting and a medium stiff brush and fine emery will be required.

A testing stand of the adjustable type will also be necessary for tests of the completed clocks before re-fixing them in their cases. A high stand, or "horse", is necessary for testing long-case or "grandfather" clocks.

CHAPTER 3

Cleaning Simple Clocks

THE general method of cleaning a modern domestic clock is very much the same for all types and makes. Most of the modern factory-made clocks have plates and brass parts that are either lacquered or finished in some similar manner, and the cleaning involves the removal of the surface dirt and the old dried-up oil. This necessitates the washing of each part in petrol or benzine, and the careful brushing of every component to dislodge any dirt that may be clinging to corners or ridges, or to the wheel teeth or pinion leaves.

Some of the older types of domestic timekeepers such as English "dial" clocks, long-case (or "grandfather"), and bracket clocks, and French mantel and carriage clocks, need rather more extensive treatment, for their plates and parts are usually of polished brass, and so need to be repolished with metal-polish. This makes the work rather more laborious than that needed by a modern clock, and the process will be dealt with later in this book.

The best clock for the beginner is a simple modern pendulum timepiece, such as that illustrated in Figs. 1 and 2. By cleaning such a clock as this, the learner will become familiar with handling the various parts, and will then be able to proceed to more complicated work.

To begin with, the movement must be removed from its case. The pendulum bob should be taken off as a first step, and before the clock is moved more than is absolutely necessary, for if this is not done, the suspension spring may be buckled, and so become useless.

Next, remove the hands. The minute hand usually fits tight on a small squared portion of the projecting minute

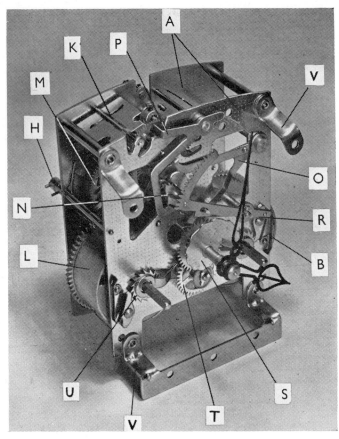

Fig. 14.—Front Plate End-view of typical 8-day Pendulum Striking Clock. Made by Smith's English Clocks Ltd.

A—Frame Plates; B—Going Barrel of Time Train; H—Striking Hammer; K—Striking Fly; L—Going Barrel of Striking Train; M—Striking Train Hammer Wheel; N—Gathering Pallet; O—Warning Detent; P—Rack Hook; R—Rack; S—Snail (on Hour Wheel of Motion Work); T—Motion Work Minute Wheel; U—Striking Winding Ratchet; V—Lugs for Attachment to Case.

Fig. 15.—Back Plate End-view of typical 8-day Pendulum Striking Clock. Made by Smith's English Clocks Ltd.

A—Frame Plates; B—Going Barrel of Time Train; C—Intermediate Wheel of Time Train; D—Crutch; E—Pendulum Rod; F—Suspension Spring; G—Back Cock, or pallet Cock; H—Striking Hammer; J—Warning Wheel of Striking Train; K—Fly.

spindle, and is kept in place by either a collet and tapered pin, or a small knurled nut. Remove whichever of these is fitted, and then carefully pull the hand off the square. After the minute hand is off, the hour hand can usually be pulled off the pipe on which it fits. It is almost always a push-fit, and gentle pulling, with, if necessary, a slight twisting motion, will soon bring it off.

After the hands are off, turn to the back of the clock, and remove the screws of the lugs which hold the clock to its case. When these are out, remove the clock movement from the case, taking care not to bend any part in the process.

When the movement is out of its case, examine it carefully, noting the position of all the components and the way they engage with one another. The wise repairer also looks carefully for possible faults, for the detection of these at this early stage will save a lot of trouble during subsequent work. Note any component that seems broken or damaged. Examine all wheels and pinions for bent or broken teeth or leaves. Next put on a key, and test to see if the mainspring is broken.

If it is (a thing that will be obvious from the ease with which the key can be turned), examine the teeth of the main-wheel and the next pinion and wheel to see if any are bent or broken off. Such damage frequently happens when a mainspring breaks. If such damage *is* found, new parts may be essential.

Do *not*, at this stage, attempt to loosen any of the nuts or screws securing the frame, or any part of the winding ratchet mechanism, for the mainspring may be fully wound. There is a lot of power in a wound mainspring, and if this is suddenly released, it can wreck the clock, and also injure the repairer.

Before the clock can be taken down, the power of the mainspring must be let down, and this needs care. Put a key on the winding square, hold the key firmly, and keep a firm hand on the clock movement. Then, gently lift the ratchet pawl (which is known to clockmakers as a "click"), and carefully allow the key to turn back about half a turn. Let the click re-engage securely with the ratchet wheel, take a fresh grip on the key, and repeat the process until the spring is right down. Make sure that the click re-engages securely with the ratchet wheel each time, and do not attempt to let the spring down more than half a turn at a time. Take every care. A slip at this point may be an unpleasant experience.

Once the spring has been let down and its power released, disassembly of the movement can proceed quite swiftly. Remove the two screws that hold the small bracket, or "cock", which carries the suspension-spring pillar, and the rear pivot hole of the pallet spindle. Take this cock off, and carefully remove the pallets, uncoupling them from the pendulum rod and taking care not to damage the suspension spring.

Next, the winding ratchet wheel and its retaining bar can be removed, and after that, the main frame nuts on the pillars can be taken off. As soon as this is done, the plates can be separated and the wheels and pinions removed. Place all the parts in a box to prevent them from getting lost.

Remove the cover which will be found on one end of the going barrel, the best method of doing this being by inserting a short lever into the slot provided and gently prising up. Then unhook the spindle (the "barrel arbor") and remove it. Then carefully ease the mainspring out of the barrel, a turn at a time. Take care not to strain the spring, particularly when you arrive at the point where it is hooked to the wall of the going barrel, and note which way the spring end hooks on to the "barrel hook" in the barrel wall.

Next take off the motion-work wheels and pinions, and extract the pin which holds the flat "set-hands" spring against the "centre" wheel. Disassembly is now complete.

Now proceed with the cleaning. Place about half a cupful

of petrol or benzine in a suitable bowl, and place the parts in the petrol to soak for a short time. Then, with a small brush, carefully remove dirt and old oil from every place where it can cling. A small paint brush, such as a Harris ½-inch bristle brush, is ideal for getting right into all inaccessible corners, but such a brush should be bought for this special job, and never used for any other. It must also be washed out and kept perfectly clean.

When the parts are washed and brushed clean, a piece of clean white cloth and some tissue paper will help in getting the parts dry, and they should then be brushed with a very clean medium-stiff clock brush. As each part is finished, it should be placed in a clean box, which should be covered with a lid if the work has to be interrupted, even for a short while. The utmost cleanliness—even a sort of *surgical* cleanliness—is desirable.

Cleaning the mainspring is not so easy as the cleaning of other parts. It is not advisable to place it in petrol or benzine, for this seems to increase its tendency to break. Nor is it wise to straighten the spring unduly. At the same time, the spring must be clean. Old oil or greasy dirt may cling firmly to the spring surfaces, and can cause them to bind together in operation, causing much waste of power. So, it is best to fasten one end of the spring to some fixture, and then to work carefully along its length, cleaning all dirt off. In some cases, this dirty film may cling almost like a coat of vanish and prove most difficult to remove.

When a spring is found to be coated like this, pumice powder, mixed with thin oil, or even with petrol, should be used to clean it. Put a small amount of the mixed powder and oil on a pad of rag, and work slowly along the coils, using moderate pressure. Sometimes hard patches of dried-up grease will be found, and these must all be cleaned off. Be careful to clean off every bit of the abrasive after the cleaning is completed by wiping the spring with clean rag.

Clean all the pivots of wheels and peg out all holes in the plates with a sharpened piece of peg-wood. Make sure that all the surfaces and edges of the plates are clean, and wipe everything with a clean rag.

Before starting on reassembly, it is as well to test each wheel separately in the plates, to make sure that none of the pivot holes is worn, for if any of the pivot holes are worn oval, they will need to be bushed. Instructions for this work are given later in this book. See that all pivots are clean and that none is bent. If any bent pivots are found, they must be carefully straightened, preferably by pliers that have brass jaws. These will not damage the surfaces of the pivots. Pivots that are worn or ridged must be smoothed and re-burnished, or, if seriously cut, they must be replaced. Re-pivoting is one method of effecting a good repair, but this calls for considerable skill with a lathe. On most modern clocks, the simplest way is to obtain a complete replacement wheel and pinion.

Assuming that all pivots and pivot holes are in order, and that no defects are present on other parts, reassembly can be proceeded with. First, replace the spring in its barrel. This is done by hooking the hooking hole at the outer end on to the hook in the wall of the barrel (taking care that the spring is hooked to coil in the right direction), and then gently feeding in the coils, a little at a time, until the whole spring is home in the barrel. Take care not to strain or distort the spring, and be careful that it does not fly out again. Winding in is a job requiring care, but it is really a case of acquiring the right knack. A skilled repairer can do the job in a minute or two, but a beginner may take far longer.

Once the spring is in, settle it finally in place by tapping the end of the barrel smartly on a block of hard wood. Then insert the central spindle, or "arbor", pour in about ten or twelve drops of clock-oil, see that the hook on the arbor engages with the hole in the inner end of the spring and replace the cover. This may take a little humouring to get home, but if it cannot be pressed in to snap into its groove in the barrel edge by reasonable pressure with a piece of hard wood, it may be gently squeezed home in a vice. Take care to pad the jaws of the vice with pieces of rag, or the barrel and cover will be marked.

The best way to get a stubborn barrel cover home in a vice is partially to insert the cover, and then to grip the portion that will not go in in the vice, slowly screwing up the vice jaws until the cover snaps home. It may be necessary to move the barrel round, and coax the cover home in stages. At all costs, avoid distorting the cover.

With the barrel cover in place, oil the points where the arbor pivots in barrel and cover, and work the oil into the bearings by turning the arbor slightly.

Replacement of the components of the train in the frame can now be proceeded with. Put the centre wheel and pinion on its spindle. Sometimes a small washer is interposed between the end of the centre pinion and the shoulder on the spindle against which it locates. If this washer was fitted, do not forget to replace it. If the washer was *not* originally provided, it may even be an advantage to fit one.

Next replace the domed friction spring which provides the set hands grip. When it is in place, press it gently but firmly against the centre wheel until it is compressed far enough to enable the retaining pin to be inserted into the hole in the spindle. See that the pin fits snugly into the recess in the centre of the spring.

Put the barrel in place, and follow with the intermediate wheel and the third and escape wheels. It is best to place these parts in position in the front plate, being careful not to bend any pivots as they are fitted into their pivot holes.

Next start to place the back plate in position and carefully lead each back pivot into its pivot hole. Hold the front and back plates together gently while this is being done, but do not use *too much* pressure, or pivots may be bent. It may be helpful to put on one or more of the retaining nuts, threading them a turn or two on to the pillar ends, which will be projecting slightly through their holes in the back plate.

When the train has all its pivots safely home in their holes, the other frame nuts can be put in position, and tightened up. Test the train as the tightening proceeds, and again when all the nuts are tight, to make sure that each wheel revolves freely. Make sure, too, that each wheel arbor has a slight amount of endway movement, known as "endshake", between the plates. There should not be too much of the movement, but there must be sufficient to ensure freedom.

Next, replace the winding ratchet wheel and its retaining bar, putting a little oil on the front pivot of the barrel arbor where it bears in the front plate before putting the wheel in position. See that the pawl, or click, engages securely with the ratchet wheel teeth, and is properly pressed against the wheel by the click spring. If the spring does not press the click firmly enough bend it slightly to give it a little extra tension.

After this, the pallets can be replaced and their cock screwed up. Before this is finally tightened, adjust the pallet depth in its engagement with the escape wheel teeth to allow the teeth to escape correctly. This is done by setting the pallets to allow the wheel teeth just a slight amount of drop as they leave the pallets. Do not set the pallets so close to the teeth that there is any risk of them catching, and do not, on the other hand, allow the drop to be excessive. If the tips safely clear, the adjustment is correct. Test the clearance all round the wheel before passing the adjustment as correct.

Apply a small drop of oil to each pivot of the train, and to the pallet pivots. Oil also the pivot pin or screw of the click, and the point where the click spring presses on the click. Oil the pallets and the pivot points of the motion work, and the friction points of the set hands clutch. Fit the pendulum rod to the crutch, and hook the rod on to the suspension spring. This completes the assembly.

The movement should next be carefully checked over, to make sure that everything is in order, that all nuts and screws are tight, and that no point requiring oil has been missed. Having satisfied himself on these points, the repairer can proceed with the work of replacing the clock in its case, or, if a suitable stand can be arranged, giving it a short test run. If this can be done, it is a wise thing to do, for it may save having to remove the clock from its case if any defect shows up.

Assuming all is well, the clock can be screwed home in its case, care being taken to ensure that the winding square and hand spindles come correctly in the centre of their holes in the case. If they do not, adjustment of the movement attachment lugs will usually correct the trouble.

With the movement in place, put the hour hand and minute hand in position. Take care that both are pushed right home, and fix the minute hand by its collet and pin, or its small screwed nut, whichever is fitted.

Put on the pendulum bob, and adjust the crutch until the clock beats, or "ticks", evenly. Go to work carefully when making this adjustment, for if the crutch is handled carelessly, the suspension spring may be damaged.

This completes the actual work of cleaning, and after regulation has been carried out, the job is done.

CHAPTER 4

Cleaning Dutch Clocks

A FAMILIAR form of an old-fashioned Dutch clock is illustrated by Figs. 16 to 18, the movement, or works, being shown with the parts named. The framework and part of the wheelwork, too, are of wood, and the pivot holes are little pieces of brass tube inserted into holes in the wood. The pivots are steel pins driven into the centres of the wheels, and the pinions are formed on wooden bodies. In some very old Dutch clocks, the wheels themselves, except the escape wheel, are of wood.

To clean one of these clocks, first detach the weight and pendulum; next unscrew the nut that holds on the minute hand, take off the hands, turn the clock over on to its face, and remove the pins that fasten the front of the clock case to the body. Pull them out boldly with a pair of pliers, and then take off the motion work. For removing the train wheels, one of the centre wooden uprights will be found to come out. Take out a pin near the top end, and

Fig. 16.—Front View of typical Dutch Clock. Note the Cast Brass Hands and Bezel, and Chains used to transmit drive to the Time-keeping and Striking Chains.

Fig. 17.—Typical Dutch Clock. View of left-hand side of movement, showing "end-to-end" mounting of Trains.

A—Wooden Main Frame. Made of Bars inserted into Top and Bottom Plates; B—Wooden Back-Plate, pierced at top for Clock to be hung on wall; C—Suspension Pillar for Pendulum; D—Distance Pillars, to hold movement away from wall; E—Main Wheel of Timekeeping Train. Arbor is of wood; F—Second Wheel of Timekeeping Train. Note Wooden Lantern Pinion; G—Escape Wheel; H—Pallet Arbor; I—Crutch; J—Main Wheel of Striking Train; K—Second, or Cam-Wheel, of Striking Train; L—Warning Wheel of Striking Train; M—Fly of Striking Train; N—Pinion on Striking Main Wheel which drives Locking-Plate Wheel; O—Locking-Plate; P—Bell; Q—Cannon Pinion; R—Minute Wheel and Pinion (this lets off Striking Train); S—Hour Wheel; T—Dial.

Fig. 18.—Typical Dutch Clock. Viewed from the right-hand side, and showing the Warning and Locking Detents and unusual "Right-angle" Hammer lifting action.

A—Wooden Main Frame; B—Wooden Back-Plate; C—Suspension Pillar; D—Distance Pillars; G—Escape Wheel; K—Second Wheel of Striking Train (the Cams on this raise and lower Detent "X"); L—Warning Wheel (which also locks the Striking Train, by engaging with the tip of Detent "X"); M—Fly; P—Bell; R—Minute Wheel and Pinion; S—Hour Wheel; T—Dial and Wooden Bezel; U—Striking Hammer; V—Striking Hammer lifting Detent; W—Warning Let-off Detent; X—Locking Detent; Y—Striking Hammer Return Spring; Z—Glass, set in Brass Bezel pull towards the worker, and it will come out. Care must be taken not to bend the pivots of any of the wheels.

Clean all the wheelwork as already described for the simple spring-driven timepiece, and make a thorough examination as before. The pallets are sure to be cut more or less, and if they will not bear flatting down with the emery stick, a new pair of pallets is necessary. These can easily be made from a strip of tool steel, which should be heated and bent to match exactly the shape of the unworn parts of the old pallets. When shaping is completed, drill the small hole needed to rivet them to their spindle, and then temporarily mount them up for a test. If all is satisfactory they can be hardened, tempered to a light straw, and permanently fixed to the spindle. Making such pallets is excellent practice for more ambitious work.

In these clocks the pallets are often found to have worked loose, and require riveting up again. Beyond that, and the wear of the escapement, there will probably be not much the matter with them. The escape depth can be adjusted by knocking down the bearing of the front pallet pivot. Thoroughly clean the pendulum suspension wires and give them a little oil.

Many Dutch clocks are fitted with striking mechanism of the "locking-plate" type. An example is shown in the illustrations. The construction of this striking mechanism is very similar to that used for other striking clocks, and the instructions given in the chapter on striking work should be studied before this part of the clock is dealt with.

A little fine emery-cloth will improve the appearance of the hands and the brass rim round the glass. As in all clocks, see that it is "in beat" when hung up level. If the pendulum-bob is found to be loose, and drops down, tighten by inserting a piece of cork between it and the pendulum-rod.

CHAPTER 5

Cleaning French Clocks

THE ordinary French timepiece movement, as found usually in a case of wood or black marble, was one of the most popular types at the turn of the century. Many thousands of these well-made and reliable timepieces are in use all over the world. They are good timekeepers, their fairly good wheels and pinions and heavy pendulums enabling them to keep correct to within a minute or two a week. They go for eight days, often for fourteen and occasionally for twenty-eight days.

To take out the movement, open the back door and remove the two screws, found one on each side, which hold the movement and prevent its falling forward. Unhook and take off the pendulum, and then draw the movement out from the front of the case. It will be found to be held in place by two brass arms. Take off the hands by unpinning the minute hand, and removing it and the hour hand. The movement can then be unpinned from the frame which holds the dial, etc., and the latter put on one side.

The cheapest class of French movements have rough-filed plates and wheels, and rough motion-work (hand work). The motion wheels are placed between the plates, and there is a set-hand arrangement somewhat similar to that found in an American clock—that is, the centre wheel turns friction-tight upon its spindle. In the better grades of French movement quite a different arrangement is found, the centre wheel being fast upon its spindle, and the motion wheels placed between the front plate and the dial, after the manner adopted in a watch. In either case, the hands should not be too easy; if they are, the grip of the set-hands clutch must be tightened, either by slightly nipping

37

Fig. 19.—Front View of typical French Clock, with Pendulum and Rack Striking Mechanism.

A—Frame Plates; B—Frame Pillars; C—Going Barrel of Timekeeping Train; D—Intermediate Wheel of Timekeeping Train; E—Cannon Pinion (on extended Centre Arbor); F—Minute Wheel and Pinion of Motion work; H—Hour Wheel, carrying Stepless Snail of Striking Work; J—Timekeeping Train Winding Square, Ratchet Wheel, etc.; K—Striking Train Winding Square and Ratchet Wheel, etc.; L—Warning Detent; M—Striking Rack; N—Rack Hook; O—Gathering Pallet; P—Detachable Cock for Third Arbor of Timekeeping Train; Q—Adjustable Block carrying Pivot Hole for Pallet Pivot; R—Spindle of Regulating Adjustment Control; S—Rear Pallet Cock, carrying Suspension Regulation Attachment.

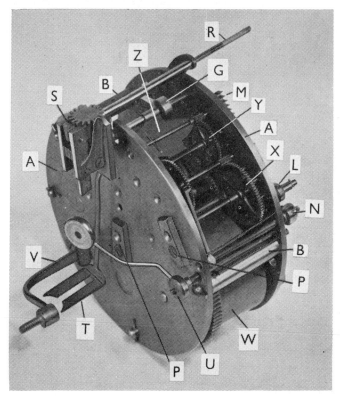

Fig. 20.—Three-quarter Rear View of typical French Clock, with Pendulum and Rack Striking Mechanism.

A—Frame Plates; B—Frame Pillars; L—Warning Detent; M—Striking Rack (edge only showing); N—Rack Hook, with Train Locking Detent shown between the Clock Plates; P—Detachable Cocks for Rear Pivots of Centre Arbor and Striking Train Hammer Wheel Arbor; R—Spindle of Regulating Adjustment Control; S—Rear Pallet Cock, with Suspension Block embodying a Suspension Regulating Attachment; T—Crutch; U—Striking Hammer; V—Bell Stud; W—Striking Train Going Barrel; X—Striking Train Hammer Pin Wheel; Y—Striking Warning Wheel; Z—Striking Fly.

the sleeve attached to the centre wheel, or by similarly nipping the thinned down central part of the minute wheel sleeve on the motion-work, according to which form is fitted to the clock.

The winding work—that is, the ratchet and click, etc.— will be found on the outside of the front or back plate, according to whether the clock winds from the front or back. Before the clock can be taken apart the mainspring must be let down. Place the key on the winding square, and, taking off the pressure from the click, hold the click up with the finger, and allow the key to go back half a turn, letting the click fall back into its place again. Repeat this operation until the spring is completely unwound. The back cock can then be unscrewed and the pallets taken out, the pins can be withdrawn and the plates taken apart, and the clock will then be in pieces.

If all the pivots and wheels are right, and the mainspring not broken, cleaning may be proceeded with. The rough movements referred to in the foregoing can be cleaned by immersing them in petrol and then pegging out. The barrel and mainspring, however, must not be put into petrol, but wiped clean, and brushed outside with the chalk brush and dry chalk. The arbor and cover can be washed in petrol, and cleaned thoroughly before being replaced. Put plenty of clock oil on the mainspring before putting on the barrel cover, and do not forget to oil the barrel-arbor pivots.

If any difficulty is experienced in getting the barrel cover off, hold the barrel in the hand, cover up, and knock the arbor sharply on a hard-wood block, driving off the cover at one blow.

If the mainspring is very dirty remove it from the barrel and clean it. The method of doing this is similar to that described in Chapter 3.

To clean the better class of French movements (those with polished plates), a different method is pursued. At least three brushes will be required. Strip the plates, that is, unscrew everything upon them, and mix a little rotten stone powder with sweet-oil (olive or salad oil) to a paste. Put some of this on a rottenstone brush, and vigorously brush the plates and brass wheels, cocks, etc., brushing backwards and forwards straight from top to bottom, to put on an even grain. This done, put all into a hand-bowl containing petrol, and with a brush thoroughly wash all rottenstone and grease from the parts. Take them out and dry with a clean cloth, and put on one side for a few minutes for the last traces of the petrol to dry off. Do not put the barrel into the liquid, but with the rottenstone brush nearly dry, polish its sides, and clean off with the petrol brush rather dry, afterwards wiping clean with the cloth. All being dry, take the chalk brush and dry chalk, and proceed to brush up and polish all the parts; then peg out all pivot-holes clean, also between the leaves of pinions, and brush through all wheel teeth, to remove any traces of rottenstone.

The clock can next be put together, applying a little clock oil to pivots and pallets, and just a trace to the crutch where the pendulum hangs.

The pendulum suspension-spring must be treated very carefully, or it may easily be spoilt, for once damaged it cannot be corrected. In putting the clock back in its case, see that the 12 o'clock is quite upright, and then set in beat by slightly bending the crutch as usual.

French clocks have an excellent regulating arrangement which is turned by a small key from the front. Turning to the right shortens the acting part of the pendulum suspension-spring, and so makes the clock go faster, whilst turning to the left has the opposite effect. The entire arrangement is contained in the "back cock", and must be taken apart and carefully cleaned with the rest.

CHAPTER 6

Cleaning English Clocks

CLEANING "Eight-day Dial" Clock. — English clocks are of various patterns, but one style of workmanship will be found in most of them. The ordinary eight-day English shop or kitchen clock, commonly known as an "eight-day dial", is well and solidly made, is a good time-keeper, and will last a lifetime. Its mechanism is extremely simple, and there is very little to get out of order.

There is one point of design in which the English dial clock differs from those previously described. This is the "fusee", a most ingenious arrangement, designed to make use of the principle of the moment of a force to overcome variations in the driving power of a mainspring.

As mentioned in Chapter 1, the power of even the best mainspring decreases as it runs down, and this lessening of power can affect the timekeeping of the clock it is driving, particularly towards the end of its run.

To compensate for this, the spring of an English dial clock (and of some other types as well), is arranged to drive the main wheel through a "fusee". This consists of a spirally-grooved brass drum of conical form, mounted on the same arbor as the main wheel, and linked to the main wheel by a ratchet mechanism of the usual type. The groove begins at the large diameter of the cone, and ends at the small diameter.

The mainspring is mounted in a separate barrel, which is of uniform diameter throughout, and has a smooth surface. This barrel is linked to the fusee by a line (or a chain), one end of which is attached to the barrel, and the other end to the large diameter of the fusee. When the spring is run down, almost the whole length of the line is coiled round the smooth outer surface of the barrel.

Winding is carried out by rotating the fusee, and as the line is wound off the barrel and on to the fusee, it is coiled around the progressively decreasing diameter of the fusee groove. The running of the clock reverses this process, gradually unwinding the line from the fusee, and allowing it to coil on the surface of the barrel.

From this, it will be understood that, when the mainspring is exerting its greatest power, it will be driving the main wheel through the smaller end of the fusee, and then, as its power decreases, its leverage increases in proportion. As the curve of the conical part of the fusee is made to increase in the correct ratio to the decrease in the power of the spring, the drive to the main wheel remains practically constant.

To prevent the line from being wound right off the smaller end of the fusee, the line is arranged to operate a stop-finger, which prevents overwinding.

The weakest point is the gut line, which chafes through after a few years' wear. In the best clocks the gut is replaced by a steel chain, which is a great improvement.

To take such a clock apart, first remove the pendulum, and unpin the minute hand and remove it. The hour hand is held by a small screw, which should be withdrawn, and the hand taken off. Then lay the clock upon its face, remove the four wooden pegs at the sides, and lift the back of the case right off. The square movement itself will be found to be pinned to the dial and front part of the case. Remove the four pins from the dial feet, and it will come off altogether, leaving the dial alone screwed to the front of the case. This can be put on one side. Do not attempt to let the spring down, but put a little oil on the pivots, and, having removed the motion-work and the pallets, let the clock run down. As it does so, notice if the wheels and pinions run smoothly, and if they are true. When quite run down, put a hand-vice or a large key on the square of the barrel arbor, and raise the click, letting the spring down gently. The plates can then be unpinned, and the clock taken apart. The parts may be cleaned with rottenstone, etc., as described in other chapters.

Before putting together, look to the pallets, and smooth out any marks of wear; examine the pinions, and if any are badly cut, the wheels had better be shifted along their arbors to work in another place. Sometimes these are soldered on, and shifting them gets them out of truth. In that case nothing can be done unless the wheel seat is turned afresh; a shoulder would be turned to receive the wheel tightly, and then be riveted over with a punch. Look for wide pivot holes, and if there are any bad ones, bush them as described later in this book. Then put the barrel, fusee, and wheels in position between the plates, and pin together.

Next carefully wind the gut on the barrel, turning the latter with a key; and when all is wound on, put on the outside ratchet, and wind it, or "set it up", about half a turn. Pin the ratchet on, and screw the click tight; then put in the pallets, and wind the clock up. In doing this,

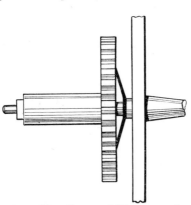

Fig. 21.—Cannon Pinion and Setting Spring of English Clock.

the gut must be carefully guided on to the fusee, and not on any account be allowed to run off or drag in a slanting direction. The best way to guide it is to hold a smooth file-handle, or something of a like nature, against it during the winding, bearing sideways upon it, to keep it straight.

Where there is a chain instead of a gut

line, first hook the chain in the barrel and wind it all upon it, then hook it in the fusee, and then proceed as before explained. Oil all pivots, pallets, etc., and put on the motion work. Note the short setting spring that goes on under the cannon pinion, as in Fig. 21. By no means put it on the wrong side up, or the clock will certainly stop. The two ends of the spring should bear on the under side of the cannon pinion. When all together, and ready to hang up, see that the crutch is free in the slot in the pendulum, and does not touch either at the top or bottom, nor stick in it. Just a trace of oil should be put upon the pin. To set these clocks in beat, the crutch may have to be bent.

Renewing a Gut Line.—To put on a new gut line, take the movement to pieces, and take out the old one from the barrel. To get the fusee end out, the fusee must be taken to pieces. A circular piece of brass will be found outside the fusee wheel or main wheel; it is a kind of key, and requires to be unscrewed or un-pinned and then taken off. While it is off it can be cleaned, and the ratchet and click-work oiled. Obtain a new line (Fig. 22) of the same thickness, and measure it to correct length, allowing for fastenings. Push one end of the line in through the hole in the end of the fusee groove and then tie a knot in the

Fig. 22.—End of Gut Line.

Fig. 23.—Gut Line after searing.

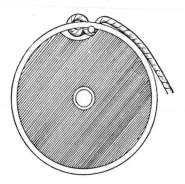

Fig. 24.—Fastening Gut at Barrel End.

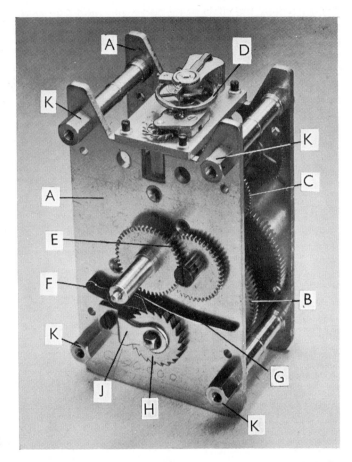

Fig. 25.—Simple 8-day Platform Lever Timepiece. Made by the Bentima Clock Co. Ltd.

A—Frame Plates; B—Main Wheel and Going Barrel; C—Third Wheel; D—Platform Lever Escapement; E—Motion Work Wheels and Pinions; F—Winding Click (or Pawl); G—Winding Click Spring; H—Winding Ratchet Wheel; J—Ratchet Wheel Retaining Bar; K—Frame Pillar Nuts which also serve for Attachment to Case.

line. This knot fits into the small hole in the fusee, and anchors the end of the line in position. To prevent the knot from coming undone treat the end by "searing" in the following way: get a small, flat piece of iron or brass and heat nearly to redness. Apply this to the end of the gut, which will expand into the shape shown in Fig. 23. The end cannot now pull through. Fig. 24 shows the method of fastening the barrel end, which must be seared in the same way.

Cleaning Skeleton Clock.—The mechanism of this old-fashioned kind of clock is similar to that of the "eight-day dial"; there is generally added a bell at the top and a hammer which is caused to strike one blow at each hour—not a very complicated affair. These clocks want most careful cleaning. Every part must be thoroughly well cleaned with rottenstone and polished with chalk. The edges of the piercings in the plates must be polished with strips of washleather and rottenstone, and afterwards with more leather and a peg. All steel-work needs to be polished and burnished with a burnisher and oil It is all visible, and therefore no pains should be spared in getting it up well. Thoroughly clean off all rottenstone dust, oil, or other abrasive when the polishing is completed.

CHAPTER 7

General Repair Work

APART from the relatively simple processes of cleaning and oiling, the most usual kinds of repair work that will be required by the majority of clocks will be "bushing", which means the fitting of new bearings to the pivot holes, the restoration of good bearing surfaces to pivots, the correction of wear on pinions and pallets, and the replacement of broken or fatigued mainsprings.

Much of this work can be carried out with very simple tools by any person of moderate skill, but some of it may call for skilful fitting and turning, and a fairly high standard of proficiency. It should be mentioned that the ability to use a lathe is such a tremendous asset in clock repair work as to be almost an essential accomplishment. Once the repairer has learned to handle a lathe correctly, and to do simple turning and drilling, he will be able to carry out almost all the work required on the majority of clocks swiftly and well, and to get much more real enjoyment from the job.

Bushing.—The fitting of new bushes to pivot holes is the process most commonly needed in all clock repairing. It involves the insertion into the frame plates, or similar parts, of metal sleeves, or "bushes", that will form new bearings for the pivots of the wheels and pinions.

The wear of the original pivot holes can arise from the abrasive action of grit that has entered them, from a lack of proper lubrication, or from sheer wear and tear during a long period of service. The wear almost always takes place on one side of the hole only, this being, quite naturally, the side against which the pivot is thrust by the power transmitted by the preceding wheel of the train.

48

This wear can be detected by testing the pivot for sideway rock in its hole after all power from the mainspring or weight has been removed from the clock. If the pivot has more than the very slightest sideway movement in its hole, then a new bush should certainly be fitted.

The work of fitting the bush involves the opening out of the pivot hole with a broach until a cylindrical metal sleeve with a central hole can be inserted in the plate. This sleeve is the "bush", and when it has been driven tightly home into the hole in the plate, its central hole is opened out with a broach until the pivot for which it will form a bearing is a good running fit.

When a worn pivot hole is being enlarged to prepare it for bushing, it is not good practice just to insert the broach and open out the hole until the bush can be driven in. As previously mentioned, wear in pivot holes nearly always takes place on the side against which the pivot is pressed by the driving power of the clock. If a hole that is worn in this way is simply opened out by broaching it, the position of the enlarged hole will be a compromise between the original and the worn position of the hole. This will interfere with the correct meshing, or "depthing", of the wheels and pinions concerned, and so may lead to trouble. To overcome this, worn pivot holes should be carefully inspected before being opened out, and then filed with a watchmaker's rat-tail file in the opposite direction to that in which the wear has taken place. This process is known to clock repairers as "drawing the hole", and the filing should remove an amount of metal equal to that worn away, but, of course, in the opposite direction. When this has been done, the hole may be carefully opened out with a broach until it is circular.

This calls for very cautious handling of the broach, for the hole will be oval, and the cutting edges of the broach may bite unevenly, or even tend to jam. Take very light cuts until the hole becomes circular again, and, once the hole *is* circular, do not open it out any farther until the

D

correct bush has been selected, for the latter must be a tight drive-in fit to the hole if it is to be securely fitted.

There are several forms of bushes available for repair work. One consists of lengths of brass rod, bored with a small central hole, and stocked by material dealers in a number of graded sizes. This brass rod is known as "bushing wire", and it can be cut off to any suitable length, and then driven home into the clock plate. It is most useful to the repairer who can mount it up in a lathe chuck, and turn and part it off to suit the job in hand.

Even so, a lathe is not essential when using bushing wire, for bushes made from it can be fitted by hand, and if care is taken, they should be entirely satisfactory.

Suppose a clock has a wide worn escape pivot hole. A piece of bushing wire is selected, the central hole of which will not quite go on the pivot. This is very slightly and evenly tapered down with a file on the outside at one end. The pivot hole is opened out by broaching until the bush goes in tight, not quite through the plate, oil being used with the broach. The wire is then cut off and filed on each end, so that, according to the judgment of the worker, it can be hammered into the plate flat and not project much. The bush is then inserted from the inside of the frame plate, hammered in until the inside surface is flush and level, and then riveted a little with a punch on the outside where the oil sink is. The inside surface can then be smoothed by a fine, flat file, followed by grinding with Ayr-stone or slate and water until level, and, if desired, polished with Globe metal polish on a rag. Globe metal polish, it may here be observed, does well for polishing clock plates; but should be well washed off afterwards with benzoline or petrol.

The outside surface of the bush may be chamfered out to the level of the oil-sink with a circular-faced cutting tool or drill, to form a nice finish. Finally the new bush is opened out by broaching until it fits on the pivot, and when the wheel is put in the frame it spins quite freely and has a sufficient amount of endshake. In opening out a bush by broaching to fit a pivot, the broach should be kept quite upright, or else the hole will be made too large before the wheel will spin freely.

Another way of obtaining bushes is to purchase them ready-made in boxes containing assorted sizes. This is probably the simplest and quickest method, and as the bushes are accurately turned and finished to a slight taper, it is an easy matter to select the correct size, and then to broach open the hole in the plate until the bush is a tight driving fit. When choosing a bush, select one whose central hole is somewhat smaller than the pivot that will run in it, and open out the hole after the bush is in position. If the pivot is cut or ridged, it must, of course, be smoothed and burnished before it is fitted to its new hole.

For smaller sizes of bushes, such as those of French clocks and small timepieces, assorted sets of bushes turned on the ends of short lengths of brass rod can be bought at material dealers. These can be driven home in the plates and then the brass rod can be broken off at a nick provided for the purpose. The inner surface of the bush then only needs to be smoothed down to the level of the plate in order to complete the job. Final broaching to fit the pivot provides a first-class bush.

When the broaching is completed, a small counter-sinking tool should be used to produce a small chamfer on the inner side of the pivot hole, and another, rather larger, on the outside to serve as an oil-retaining sink. If a really high finish is required, the hole may be given a final burnishing with a "smoothing" or "burnishing" broach, a tool that can be obtained from material dealers.

Repairing Pivots.—The most usual damage to pivots is the destruction of their polish, or even the ridging or scoring of the surfaces to an extent that may seriously reduce their size. The cause of the trouble is dirt and lack of proper lubrication, and if the clock has been running under these conditions for some time, the surfaces may be grooved so deeply that the pivots are useless. Few defects in clock mechanism are more serious than badly scored pivots.

If a pivot is only lightly scored, it can often be corrected by mounting it in a lathe and carefully filing it down with a very fine pivot file until the grooves are removed. After this, the pivot will need to be re-burnished, and its pivot hole will have to be re-bushed to provide a properly fitting bearing for the slightly smaller pivot.

If a pivot is so badly scored that its diameter will be seriously reduced by the removal of the score marks, then a new arbor, or a new pivot, must be fitted. For clocks of modern manufacture, the correct replacement can usually be obtained, and it is a waste of time to attempt repair, but if no spare parts are available, the most practical method of repair may be that of "pivoting". This is done by cutting off the damaged pivot, drilling a hole into the end of the arbor, and driving in a piece of steel rod which can be turned up to form a new pivot.

Some craftsmen consider that pivoting is not good practice, but if it is skilfully done, there seems to be nothing against it, for it does save a lot of time, and prevents the scrapping of a pinion and the re-colleting of a wheel. If the pinion is also badly worn, pivoting is not worth while, but if it is in good condition, a new pivot will enable it to give further service.

Pivoting requires care, for the hole must be drilled perfectly centrally in the arbor. If the arbor is hardened, it must be softened slightly, and the first step should be to let down the temper to a light blue. Then mount the arbor carefully in the lathe, and steady it by means of a suitable hole in the drilling plate attachment. Turn off the damaged pivot, and leave the shoulder flat. Next, catch the centre with the point of a very sharp graver, and then drill down into the arbor with a sharp drill mounted in the tailstock. Choose a drill that is slightly larger in diameter than the size of the finished pivot, and proceed carefully with the drilling, using a moderate speed and plenty of lubricant.

Withdraw the drill occasionally, to clear the swarf, and do not apply any heavy pressure to the drill, or it may break off in the hole.

Drill down into the arbor for about one and a half times the external length of the pivot, or even a little deeper, to ensure that the new pivot has a secure hold in the arbor. Then file a very gradual taper on a piece of good carbon steel rod of slightly larger diameter than the drilled hole, and carefully drive it home in the hole in the arbor. Cut off, leaving the projecting part rather longer than the finished length of the new pivot, and turn a male centre on the extreme end. Finish by turning the pivot to size between centres, file up and burnish. Finally carefully part off the pivot to the correct length, and round off and burnish the end.

Before attempting to do this pivoting job on an actual clock arbor, it is a good plan to practise on a plain piece of steel rod, which should be mounted in the lathe, drilled and pivoted in the manner described. The necessary proficiency will soon be acquired.

Even if pivots are not scored or worn, it is a good plan to give them some burnishing as a regular item in the work of repairing. Use a small flat burnisher, and do not apply heavy pressure, or more harm than good may be done to the surfaces. Light pressure, fairly high speed of rotation of the pivot, and the slightest trace of oil on the burnisher should produce a high burnish.

Some craftsmen prefer to finish the surfaces of pivots by polishing them. This is also a good method, but great care must be taken to remove every trace of the abrasive when the job is completed, or it may afterwards cause trouble.

The process of polishing begins by smoothing with oilstone dust and oil mixed into a paste and spread on a flat steel polisher made of soft mild steel. This has its surface filed flat to impart a slight grain and give a hold to the polishing material. The polisher may be 8 in. long, $\frac{3}{16}$ in. wide, and $\frac{1}{16}$ in. thick, and is used as a file or emery

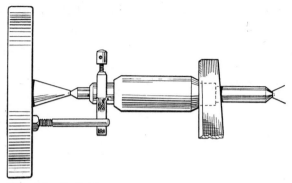

Fig. 26.—Polishing a Pivot between Lathe Centres.

stick would be, being held flat on the pivot and moved to and fro as the latter revolves in the lathe. When the oilstone dust ceases to cut, wipe it off, re-file the surface of the polisher, and apply fresh.

When smoothed until no cuts or turning marks remain, clean off and re-file the polisher, thoroughly clean the pivot, and charge the polisher afresh with a paste made of red-stuff and oil. Red-stuff is a polishing medium bought at clock-material shops, and looks like dark rouge. Use this in the same manner as before, until a brilliant polish is obtained on the pivot.

This polishing process would be altogether out of place in a cheap American or Continental clock, but is worth doing in a good movement. A section of the polisher as it lies on a pivot in the lathe is shown in Fig. 26. A bevel will be noticed on the edge that touches the pivot shoulder.

A rough-and-ready way, better than none at all, is to file and burnish worn pivots down by hand, holding the arbor in a pin-vice, and resting the pivot on a box-wood block in the bench vice. When very carefully done this is passable, and is often the readiest way to do up a pallet staff pivot that has a long crutch fixed to it, and cannot easily be revolved in a lathe. But to make a really good job of such a pivot the crutch must be got off somehow if possible, and put on again after the pivot has been burnished.

Worn Pinions.—Strictly, there is no really satisfactory way of repairing a badly worn leaved pinion, for, if long wear has deeply pitted the leaves, the accurate form, so necessary for the correct transfer of power from wheel to pinion, has been destroyed, and no attempt to reshape the leaves can restore it.

A slightly worn pinion may respond to skilful treatment, but unless the repairer is adept at the work, and has a sound knowledge of the principles of gearing, he may do more harm than good. A worn pinion on a modern movement should be replaced by the correct spare-part, and most material dealers and manufacturers carry full stocks of such spares.

Worn pinions on other clocks should be replaced by obtaining a suitably sized "rough" (i.e. unfinished) pinion from a material dealer. This will be supplied with the pinion finished and polished, but with the rest of the arbor just rough-turned. It should have a rough collet fitted to it and this collet, the arbor itself, and the pivots should be turned up in the lathe, using the old pinion as a pattern. The wheel can then be trans-

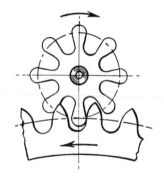

Fig. 27.—Eight-leaved Pinion meshing with Clock-wheel correctly depthed.

ferred from the old collet to the new one, and the collet riveted over and trimmed up. All this is simple lathe work, which should not present any difficulty. It must be emphasized, however, that the new pinion must be of *exactly* the same size as the old one, and that "near enough' will *not* do. When ordering the new pinion, it is best to send the old one to the material dealer as a pattern, for merely to quote a gauge size or a measurement is to invite mistakes.

In many cases, the most expeditious way of dealing with

Fig. 28.—Piece of Pinion Wire centred for mounting in the Lathe.

defective pinions in older types of clocks is to enlist the help of one of the firms who specialize in repairs of this kind. They should be sent the old pinion, the wheel with which it engages, and the clock-frame plates and pillars, and they will then supply and fit a new pinion at quite moderate cost.

Lantern pinions, in which the "leaves" consist of a number of steel pins whose ends are let into a ring of equidistantly spaced holes in two brass collars, or "shrouds", are quite easy to repair.

Worn, bent, or broken pins should be removed, and it is best to fit an entirely new set. The holes in the shrouds are usually drilled right through one shroud, and part way through the other. The pins are inserted through the shroud that is drilled right through, and when in

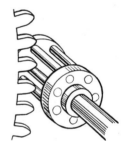

Fig. 29.—"Lantern" Pinion.

place, are retained by knurling over the outer face of this shroud to close the ends of the holes.

If the lantern pinion is a small one, not subjected to much power, it is usually possible to draw the shroud with the knurled end away from the other sufficiently to release the pins. This job should be done very carefully by holding the shroud by its rim in a pair of brass-lined pliers, or between the brass-lined jaws of a small vice.

Slight and very gentle twisting usually assists in drawing the shrouds apart, but this should be done very carefully, so as not to strain the arbor.

As soon as the shrouds are separated enough to enable the pins to be removed, take them out. Then, taking the diameter of one of the old pins as a guide, select a suitable piece of steel wire for the new pins. The original pins are often of soft material, but it is best to make the new ones from a length of the blued steel wire that can be bought from material dealers. The new pins must be exactly the same size as the old ones.

Using the length of the old pins as a pattern, cut off a set of new ones, and trim up any burrs on their ends. Insert the new pins carefully, making sure that their ends fit properly into the holes in both shrouds. Then, going very carefully to work, bring the shroud that was moved away back to its original position. Take care not to use too much force, or to move the shroud so far that the ends of the pins are forced through the knurling, and be sure that the holes are in line, or the pins will be out of proper alignment.

In the case of larger lantern pinions, which carry a lot of power, it may be unwise to disturb the shrouds, and the replacement of the pins of such pinions is best done by carefully clearing the burrs from the holes in the knurled shroud and then extracting the pins through the shroud. After the new pins have been pushed right home, the knurling should be re-done, and then each pin should be tested to make certain that it is securely retained in place.

Mainsprings.—One of the jobs which the repairer will often be called upon to do will be the replacement of broken mainsprings. This is not a difficult task, but, as the spring supplies the power to drive the clock, the replacement must be properly suited to its work. Most of the mainsprings of modern clocks are enclosed in barrels, and when such a spring breaks, it may easily bend or break some of the teeth of the main wheel, or do other damage.

For this reason, do not assume that the broken spring is the only damaged part. Check over all other parts even more carefully than usual, and take nothing for granted. The hook which links the spring to the barrel, and the pinion on the arbor next the main wheel are both very liable to damage from mainspring breakage.

If only a new spring is needed, remove the broken one from the barrel and, unless it is obviously of wrong size or strength, use it as a pattern for the replacement. Measure thickness, preferably with a micrometer, and note its width, known in the trade as its "height", and make sure that the new spring is of the same dimensions. Make certain, too, that the new spring is not much longer or shorter than the one it replaces.

When the new spring is obtained, carefully clean it before inserting it in the barrel, for it may be coated with grease, which must be removed. Then hook the outer end over the hook in the barrel wall, and carefully coil it in, little by little, until it is all in place. Take care not to distort the spring and bend it as little as possible. If a "mainspring winder" is available, it is a useful tool, but many craftsmen wind in by hand. Put a good supply of oil on the coils of the spring, and see that the central coil and its hooking hole are correctly placed for hooking up on the barrel arbor. Snap the cover home securely, and the job is completed.

Even if the mainsprings of clocks are not broken, they should be removed from their barrels and cleaned if the best performance is to be obtained from them, and if, when removed, they seem closely coiled and very lifeless, they may quite possibly be fatigued, especially if the clock is an old one. In such a case, a new spring may prove well worth while. But, never try to obtain a better action from a clock by fitting a stronger spring than that put in by the maker.

Sometimes it may be found that a supposedly broken spring merely has its hooking hole in the outer end torn out, thus permitting the whole spring to slip round in the barrel. In these cases, the end of the spring should be softened for about an inch or two, and a new hole made.

This should not be punched in, or cracks may be formed. The best method is to drill two holes on the centre line of the width of the spring, one a little larger than the other, and then to file them towards each other until they are shaped into a pear-shaped hole. Avoid any sharp corners to the hooking hole, for these may start cracks and lead to another breakage.

In many modern clocks, especially chiming clocks, the fitting of new springs is made much easier by the use of "removable barrels". The spring barrels are so constructed that they can be taken out of the frames without dismantling the movement. This is done either by making the barrel-arbors in two parts, or by fitting two small extra plates which carry the barrels. This feature should be looked for, for it saves a lot of time, not only in replacing main-springs, but in assembling the clock after an overhaul. The barrels can be fitted after the rest of the movement is assembled, a very convenient way of doing things.

Smoothing Pallet Faces.—Steel pallets are, or should be, quite hard, and therefore cannot be filed. They can be smoothed down level with emery sticks (paper on wood), or by a soft-iron polisher like the pivot polisher already described, but larger and wider, used with a paste of emery and water. To polish them, for ordinary clocks use a finer emery stick, and a finer still, until a 0/3 is used to finish, the strokes being made lengthwise on the pallet faces and not across them. This emery stick will leave almost a polish. For a clock of special quality follow this with a flat pivot polisher and red-stuff and oil, as previously described for polishing pivots, the pallets being screwed in the bench vice.

If the pallets are deeply pitted and grooved, any attempt to remove the wear marks by grinding and polishing will reduce the depthing and spacing, and increase the "drop" of the escapement, with a bad effect on the action. The only real cure for such wear, apart from the fitting of a new pair of pallets, is to soften and close them.

By the term "closing" the pallets is meant the bending of them in to bring the acting faces to a position where they will be in correct relation to each other after the wear marks are removed by filing or grinding them out. After reshaping, they are rehardened and polished.

If the pallets are made from a steel forging or pressing, closing is worth while, and is quite effective if properly done, but if the pallets are made from a bent-up strip of steel, it may be easier to make a new pair from steel strip, using the old pair as a guide. The pallets should be hardened after shaping, and then tempered to a deep straw colour, the heat for tempering being applied to the yoke of the pallets in order to leave the pallet-pads as hard as possible. Then the acting surface of the pads must be polished before the pallets are fitted to the arbor.

The pallets of many modern movements are considerably wider than the escape wheel, and are secured to their arbor by a set-screw. This enables the pallets to be moved to bring a fresh part in line with the wheel. In some cases, more than one readjustment is possible. In any case, replacement pallets can nearly always be obtained, and so it is unnecessary to spend a lot of time on repairing the old ones.

Another way of repairing worn pallets is to reface them. This is not considered first-class practice, but will often enable a pair of pallets to be made serviceable for a considerable time. The pallets should be softened, and then the faces of both pads filed down slightly. Then pieces of fairly thin mainspring should be soldered to each pad, and the edges trimmed up level with the pads. Polishing will complete the job, which should then give quite good results.

Adjusting the Pendulum Crutch.—Pendulum clocks nearly all have a "crutch" attached to the pallets for the purpose of driving the pendulum. Sometimes the crutch is a loop or fork, in which the pendulum rod hangs. At other times the crutch has a pin that enters a slot in the pendulum rod. In both kinds the principle is the same. The crutch should not bind the pendulum rod, but be quite easy and free, and it should have hardly any perceptible side-play. If it has side-play or "shake" it will waste much of the impulse that should be transmitted to the pendulum. If it is in the least tight, it will cause such a resistance as to stop the clock.

The pendulum rod itself where the crutch touches it should be smooth and polished, and the crutch polished to diminish friction. Although the centre of suspension and motion of the pendulum is supposed to be in line with the centre of motion of the pallets, and the two should work together as one, yet in practice this is an impossibility, and there is always a little sliding friction at the point of contact of the pendulum and crutch, just sufficient for any roughness or tightness to cause stoppage. A trace of oil (not a big drop) should always be placed here.

Another little point is that the pendulum rod should not rest against the bottom of the slot in the crutch; but should be about at its centre, so that it is free to move a little backwards or forwards.

As the foregoing faults are common to all pendulum clocks, the way to remedy them will be first described, and other causes of wasted power peculiar to individual types of escapements will be left until each special escapement is treated.

Repairing a Crutch.—The inside of the fork of a crutch or a slot in a pendulum rod should be burnished smooth with an oval burnisher set in a wooden handle, using a little oil to lubricate it. A crutch that is tight may be eased by a watch-pivot file before burnishing; but care must be taken not to file much off and make it too easy. A crutch that is too wide and rattles should be filed wider on one side, and a slip of brass inserted and soft-soldered in, washing the acid off well with water after soldering. The crutch can then be opened out and burnished to fit the pendulum. Fig. 30 shows what is meant, A being the slip

Fig. 30.—Brass Slip
soldered inside Crutch.

of brass soldered in. If the crutch is a pin and the pendulum rod has a slot, the same method may be pursued and a slip inserted in the pendulum slot. Do not attempt to hammer up or squeeze up a rod or a crutch, as the slot is never smooth or parallel afterwards.

Pendulum Suspension Springs.—A faulty suspension spring will often stop a clock. The spring should be straight and have no buckle or kink in it, or the pendulum will not swing straight. It should also be easy where pinned to the top of the pendulum rod, so that when the pendulum hangs the spring goes exactly in line. Too stiff and short a spring makes the clock require more power to drive it, while a spring too long and thin allows the pendulum to wobble or roll as it swings.

There is no remedy for a buckled or kinked suspension spring; a new one must be fitted. For English eight-day dials, grandfather clocks, or bracket clocks, thin watch spring does very well. Cut off a piece to the correct length, soften it for $\frac{1}{4}$ in. at each end by heating nearly to redness in a flame, and punch a round hole at each end, broaching them out to take the pins. Suspension springs for American, French and other Continental clocks can be bought very cheaply and do not pay to make, as difficulty is found in obtaining steel spring of suitable thickness, etc.

Pendulum Rods.—Pendulum rods should be straight. If curved the pendulum has a tendency to swing in a curve or roll. The bob should be a good fit, and the rating nut and screw fairly tight. A clock with a loose bob and rating screw is a great nuisance, and difficulty will be found in regulating it.

Rating screws with poor threads, or nuts that do not turn truly, must be replaced, for it is useless to regulate a clock where such defects are present. The rating screw is one of the most important items in a pendulum clock, and must give correct control of the bob.

CHAPTER 8

Recoil Escapements and their Repair

THE escapements of domestic clocks are mainly of two forms. By far the greater number are "recoil" escapements (Figs. 31, 35 and 36); a smaller number, including the best timekeepers, are "dead-beat" escapements (Figs. 38 to 45).

Recoil and Dead-beat Escapements Compared.—A recoil escapement is so called because the 'scape wheel recoils, or goes backwards a trifle, at each beat; whereas, in a dead-beat escapement the 'scape-wheel teeth drop dead upon the locking faces of the pallets and remain stationary until the next beat. Recoil escapements are easy to make, cheap, quickly readjusted when worn, and generally easy to maintain in fairly good order; but they cause the train wheels and pinions to wear rapidly, owing to the recoil causing a grinding backwards of pinions on the driving wheels. Also, this form of escapement interferes with the free motion of the pendulum, and controls it instead of leaving the pendulum free.

Dead-beat escapements are more difficult to make correctly, are consequently more costly, and are not so readily readjusted after repair; but they require less driving power and cause less wear and tear, carrying a heavier pendulum and allowing it to swing more freely than with recoil escapements. These mechanical advantages combined result in far superior timekeeping. The best dead-beat escapements have the pallet faces, upon which the wear comes, jewelled as shown in Fig. 34, thus making the escapement almost everlasting.

When a cheap clock, such as an American spring clock without a fusee, is first wound up, the motive power is very great, and when the same clock is nearly run down,

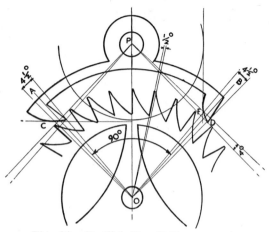

Fig. 31.—English Recoil Escapement.

the power has diminished to perhaps less than half. The effect of this with a recoil escapement and a light pendulum is to make the clock go gradually slower as it runs down. With a heavy pendulum, possibly with a dead-beat escapement, the error is less. The dead-beat escapement has a very small error in the opposite direction, and the same clock fitted with it would gradually gain as it ran down. Therefore, to keep correct time, the escapement must not have much recoil, nor must it be perfectly "dead". A cheap clock with a light pendulum should have an escapement with a moderate recoil only, and a good clock with a heavy pendulum should have a nearly dead-beat escapement, or what is known as a "half dead", that is, a dead-beat with a very slight amount of recoil on the resting surfaces, but hardly perceptible. The amount of recoil is determined by the shape of the pallets.

English Recoil Escapement

"Drop."—Fig. 31 shows an English recoil escapement as used in grandfather, eight-day dial, and English bracket clocks. It will be observed that the face of the entering pallet C lies horizontally, while that of the exit pallet D is about perpendicular. When so, the angles of impulse will be about correct, and when not so, as sometimes will be seen in clocks, the escapement is sure to be faulty. The great point to be observed carefully in this escapement, after noting the impulse faces as above mentioned, is the "drop" of the teeth on the pallets A. When a tooth passes along the face of pallet C and slides off its tip, another tooth "drops" on the face of the pallet D. And when this tooth escapes from pallet D, the next tooth in order "drops" on pallet C. The drop should be small, being just enough to ensure that as the pendulum swings, the pallet point will not catch on the back of the tooth that has just left it. A very small amount suffices for this. Then the drop on each pallet should be equal, and the drop should be equal all round the escape wheel on each tooth.

When the drop is unequal round the wheel, being slight in one place and more in another, it shows that the wheel is not true, or that it is not truly mounted on its pinion. When the wheel is not quite true it can be mounted in the lathe or turns, and rapidly revolved while a very fine file, like a watch-pivot file, is gently held to the teeth points. This should be continued until every tooth point has just been touched. This process leaves a slight burr on the teeth, and this should be removed by a watch-pivot file. If the points of any of the teeth are too thick they may be filed thinner by a half-round file, operating on the curved parts only. Do not touch the straight sides. If the drop is still unequal at different parts of it when the wheel has been topped true, it is caused by untrue mounting on its pinions, and cannot very well be altered.

As before stated, the drop should be equal on each pallet; very often it is unequal, and excessive drop on one or both pallets means power wasted. If excessive on both, the pallets may be brought nearer to the escape wheel by lowering the back cock. Bending its steady pins and filing

E

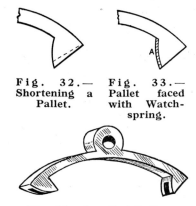

Fig. 32.— Shortening a Pallet.

Fig. 33.— Pallet faced with Watch-spring.

Fig. 34.—Jewelled Pallets.

the screw holes slightly oval will effect a little alteration. More may be done by opening out one pivot hole, filing it towards the escape wheel with a rat-tail file, and re-bushing.

When put as deep or close as it can be set, the drop may be unequal on each pallet. If it is more on pallet C, while there is hardly any at all on pallet D, a little taken off the point of pallet C will equalize matters by allowing teeth to drop off it earlier, and so give more drop on D. Then if too much on both, bring the pallets a little nearer to the escape wheel.

If the drop is too great on pallet D and just right or not enough on pallet C, take a little off the point of pallet D, as shown by the dotted line in Fig. 32, in which the effect is exaggerated. Emery sticks will make these little alterations, and should be used on the backs of the pallets, not on their impulse faces, as shown in Fig. 32. After this, see that there is no burr on the pallet corner. When made equal thus, the pallets may again need bringing a little nearer to the wheel.

If the points of any of the teeth catch, there is evidently not enough drop, and a little may be taken off the pallet back, or the pallets may be got a little farther from the wheel. Bringing the pallets nearer to the wheel will always be found to decrease the drop on C and increase that on D, so that if there is insufficient on D and too much on C, simply bringing the pallets a little closer will often do.

Remedying Worn Pallets.—When pallets have been badly worn, and the wear buffed out with emery, there is often not enough metal left in them to correct the escapement in the way just described. Then there are two courses open. The pallets may be softened by making them red-hot, closed, brought nearer to the wheel by drawing the pivot holes downwards, and then filed up to give correct impulse and drop, following the rules just explained. After this they must be hardened by heating to a bright red and plunging into water, and finally smoothed and polished with emery buffs. An easier method is to face such pallets with pieces of watch spring.

Obtain a piece of watch spring as wide as the pallet faces, file it bright on one side, and tin it with soft solder. Tin the pallet faces, and then, laying on the spring, heat gently until the spring goes down flat. If heated carefully the spring need not be softened, and will then remain at a blue temper that, though not so hard as hard steel, will yet wear for some years, and when worn may be readily replaced. After soldering wash off the acid well with plenty of water, and polish up the faces, adjusting the "drops" as before. Fig. 33 shows a pallet "faced" as described. A represents the piece of watch spring.

Another way of getting over this difficulty when the pallet faces are wide enough is to move them along on their arbor until the escape-wheel teeth work on a fresh and unworn part, when, of course, they will be correct again. A difficulty may perhaps be found in moving the pallets, as very often the brass collet to which they are riveted is brazed on. If so, perhaps the escape wheel can be moved, which will come to the same thing, but is more difficult and needs some skill. Moving a wheel collet bodily along its arbor always throws the wheel a little out of truth, and in moving an escape wheel the wheel should be taken off its collet by turning the riveted part away, the brass collet turned back so that the wheel goes farther on, and the wheel remounted and riveted on as before. After remounting, the wheel should always be "topped" as before described, and as this has a tendency to increase the drop in the escapement, moving the escape wheel is not so good a way of overcoming wear as moving the pallets would be.

Making New Pallets.—Sometimes pallets are so badly worn, and have been doctored up so many times, that there is really nothing for it but to make and fit a new pair. A steel forging can be bought at the clock-material shop, and will save much heavy filing. Before beginning work on the forging, draw out the escapement exactly to scale on writing paper. Lay the paper on the clock plate, and mark the escape and pallet pivot holes, so as to get the distance of the centres. Then enlarge the escape pivot hole truly until the arbor goes through. Push it through, and press the escape-wheel teeth points on to the paper, so as to get an impression or mark. Now taking Fig. 31, draw in the impulse face of pallet D, its point coming exactly to a tooth point. Let it be vertical and a trifle curved. Draw in the impulse face of pallet C, letting it be horizontal and also slightly curved. Its point should penetrate the escape wheel exactly midway between two teeth, and its face should just touch the tooth point before it as shown. The backs of the pallets should be straight lines pointing to the escape wheel centre. The pallet body may be drawn in any shape.

Then cut out the paper to the exact shape of the pallets. Lay it on the forging, and mark and drill the central hole, after which the outline may be scratched on the steel with a graver point, and the forging filed up to shape and size. When approaching the right size fit the rough pallets on to the arbor rather a tight fit, and place in the clock frame together with the escape wheel, and file a little off as shown to be necessary, so that the teeth can be just forced past the pallets with no drop. In this condition they may be hardened by heating to a cherry red and plunging in water. After hardening, place in the frame, and, trying as before, ease the depth and give just a little drop on each pallet by smoothing with buff sticks, finally polishing the impulse faces.

French Recoil Escapement

Setting the Depth.—Fig. 35 shows the ordinary recoil escapement found in French clocks. It acts in exactly the same way as the English recoil escapement, but the 'scape wheel has more teeth than the English one, and the pallets do not embrace so large a portion of the wheel, consequently the angles of the pallet faces are different, and cannot be relied on as an indication of correctness as in the English form. Also, being more "on the top of the wheel", placing the pallets a little closer deepens the action without very much affecting the equality of the drop on each pallet. To alter the depth, the front pallet pivot is always in an eccentric brass disc with a screwdriver slit across it, by means of which it may be turned round, and the pallets moved a trifle nearer to the wheel. When worn, these pallets become cut into grooves, which should be ground out with emery buffs, as before described, and, as they are small, great care must be taken that the corners are not unduly rounded off. After buffing and polishing, the depth will need a little readjustment by means of the eccentric disc just referred to, and if the drop becomes unequal, a trifle off one pallet back as described in connection with the English recoil escapement will correct it.

Fig.   35.—French Recoil Escapement.

Moving the Pallets.—If very badly worn, the pallets of French clocks can easily be shifted on their axis. They fit on a long tapered square, and to get them a little farther along knock them off, reduce the square just the least trifle, and knock them on again. Do not attempt to knock them farther along the tapered square without first reducing the square, or, the pallets being as hard as glass, they will very likely split across the centre hole and be in two parts.

Soldering Pallets Together.—In case such an accident

happens, the pallets can be reunited by soft-soldering, pressing them well together as the solder runs, and washing the acid off well with plenty of water, to prevent rusting. When soldered and washed, the square hole may be cleaned out with a fine file, and the pallets replaced on the arbor. Very little force must be used to drive them on, or the soldered joint will part again, so it is best to let them go on fairly easily, and set them by warming a little shellac and making sure it runs well along. The heat necessary to run the shellac will not affect the solder, and it is well to remember that shellac only requires just enough heat to make it liquid. More will only burn and destroy it, burnt shellac having no holding power.

In case this method of repairing a broken pair of pallets is not deemed good enough for the clock in hand, a new pair may be made, following the directions already given for English clock pallets.

American Recoil Escapement

These (see Figs. 36 and 37) are found in nearly all small American pendulum clocks and many of the larger ones.

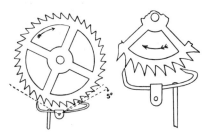

Figs. 36 and 37.—American Recoil Escapement.

It follows the same rules exactly as the French escapement, as far as setting the depth is concerned. These pallets should not be allowed to have any sideway rock on their pin pivot. Either fit a larger pin, or bush the brass holes until a good fit is obtained. Also, look particularly to the top escape-wheel pivot, and see that it has no side play. These are weak points in this escapement. Should these pallets be very unequal in their drop, it is an easy matter to soften them, bend them until correct, and re-harden them. New pallets can be bought for a few pence, therefore it is only wasted time doing much in the way of repairing old ones; but should anyone care to try, the same instructions apply as have been given in connection with the English recoil escapement.

The "American striker" is a form of general house clock. Very frequently, it is constructed for cheapness with very thin plates, consequently holes worn wide are quite common, and often cause faults in the escapement. With the hands and dial removed a general view of the escapement is attained. Move the pendulum bob in both directions until a tooth drops, and examine the crutch. The fork of the crutch should be perfectly free of the pendulum rod, with just slight shake. Too much shake is a common fault, and would cause a clock to stop. It means a loss of impulse, and will record itself by the crutch kicking. Closing the slot or fork with a pair of pliers is a simple matter; but care must be taken not to get it tight.

Lift off the pendulum bob, and move the crutch in both directions until a tooth drops, to examine the action of the escapement. The escapement should be as deep as possible to attain the least amount of drop which is required, so that the backs of the pallets are just clear of the wheel teeth. The drops must be equal on both pallets. The pin axle of the pallet centre is fixed to the pallet cock, and the latter can be shifted over nearer the centre of the escape wheel in the event of the escapement pitching too shallow.

The next procedure is to examine the pallet and escape-wheel holes. Try the side shake of both with a pair of tweezers. As the plates are very thin, the holes and pivots often become worn wide, which consequently creates a combination of faults in the escapements. To set a deeper or shallower escapement with worn-wide holes is time wasted.

CHAPTER 9

Dead-beat Escapements and their Repair

English Dead-beat Escapement

FIG. 38 shows an English dead-beat escapement, such as may sometimes be seen in a grandfather clock or an English bracket clock, and as generally used in regulators. It was invented early in the eighteenth century by George Graham, whose name is often linked with it. The term "dead-beat" is used because the escape-wheel teeth rest motionless on the faces of the pallets between each beat. Each pallet has two acting faces; one the resting or "dead" face, the other the impulse face.

Mislocking.—In these escapements the tendency of wear is to cut a groove on the dead face and across the impulse face, rounding off the corner, which should be sharp, and causing the teeth to mislock. When a tooth has traversed the impulse face of one pallet, another one should drop on the dead face of the other pallet, as near to the corner as possible without missing it. When the corner becomes worn, the teeth in dropping just miss it and fall direct on the impulse face, instead of being locked motionless on the dead face. This is termed mislocking. To remedy it, the wear must be buffed out of the impulse faces only, and the pallets closed in a vice (their central portion is generally soft enough to bend, and should first be tried with a file). Close them until the teeth just lock again. If the pallets are hard throughout, and cannot be filed anywhere, they must be removed from their arbor and softened in the centre before closing them. With care this can be done without softening the pallet faces themselves.

Alternatively, like recoil pallets, when worn they may be moved on their arbor, etc., as described in the preceding

72

chapter. The same directions also apply for topping the escape wheel, etc.

Jewelling Pallets.— Jewels are inserted in pallets to render them proof against wear (see Fig. 34). To do the work, first soften the pallets by heating. Then slit them where the teeth of the escape wheel traverse them, to a length equal to about twice the run of the teeth, the width of the slit to be one and a half times the width of the escape-wheel teeth. The slits may be cut on a wheel-cutting apparatus or by filing. Then stones—agates or onyx do very well— must be ground flat on both sides to fit the slits in the pallets, and after being ground roughly to shape to

Fig. 38.—View of typical Graham Dead-beat Escapement, with Front Plate of Clock-frame removed to show assembly

A—Frame Plate; B—Escape Wheel; C—Escape Pinion; D—Lengthened Front Escape Pivot which carries the Seconds Hand; E—Pallet Yoke; F—Exit Pallet; G—Entry Pallet; H—Pallet Arbor; J—Crutch Collet; K—Back Cock; L—Beat Adjustment Thumb-screws.

follow the outlines of the pallets, may be cemented in by warming and applying shellac. Finally the stones must have their outer surface ground down to the level of the steel pallet faces and polished, trying them in the clock frame as the grinding proceeds, to see that a correct "depth" is being made. An onyx or agate from an old signet ring is a good thing to start upon, as it is already flat on one side and of about the thickness required, and most jewellers have a few such stones amongst their odds and ends. These stones can be ground by emery powder and water on a revolving iron lap wheel or slit by a thin iron wheel fed with emery and water. Putty powder on a hard-wood wheel will polish them. During these processes a tin shield must be fitted to catch the splashings from the revolving lap wheel. The operation requires much patience, as it is a slow one.

Vienna Regulator Escapement

Dead-beat escapements of the same kind as the English, but made slightly different, are found in Vienna regulators and a few other clocks. In these the pallet bodies are often made of brass, in which the pallets lie in grooves. The pallets are curved pieces of steel, and held in place by

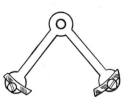

Fig. 39.—Pallets of Vienna Dead-beat Escapement

clamping screws. Fig. 39 shows such a pallet. When the faces of these become worn, the wear may be buffed out, and the pallet advanced by simply loosening the clamping screw. This obviates the necessity of softening and closing the pallets, as in those of English pattern, and is a distinct improvement. When the dead faces of these pallets become so worn that advancing them is not very satisfactory, the pallet may be reversed end for end in its groove, and has a new lease of life, being once more as new.

Many clockmakers who do not give the matter careful study complain of these clocks, and find trouble in making them work accurately. They are, as a rule, very well made, have light wheels and small pivots, and are driven by a comparatively light weight. This means that they must be kept fairly clean and well oiled; also that the pendulum cannot be expected to swing through a very large arc. As a rule, the pendulum swings very little farther than is necessary to allow the teeth to escape, and there is very little run on the locking or "dead" faces of the pallets. Therefore in these clocks always particularly try the locking of the teeth on the pallets. In many cases where they stop, the teeth lock too much; that is, they fall too far up the dead faces, and not near enough to the corners.

Fig. 40—Tooth locked properly.

Fig. 41.—Tooth locked too much.

Fig. 42.—Tooth mislocked.

This makes a larger swing of the pendulum necessary to allow them to escape, and the power not being sufficient to maintain it, the clock stops. In such cases adjust the pallets so that the teeth only just lock, and the clock will be nearly always cured. Fig. 40 shows a tooth just locking properly; Fig. 41 shows a tooth locking too far up; and Fig. 42 shows a tooth mislocking and falling on the impulse face instead of the locking face.

American Dead-beat Escapement

Some American dial clocks have dead-beat escapements, and must be served practically the same as the French clock pallets described later. In these clocks, if the pallets begin to rock sideways on their pin, a larger pin must be fitted. As in all dead-beat escapements, see that the teeth just lock and no more. Adjustment is sometimes provided for by a movable stud on which the pallets are mounted. At other times, the bar of the brass frame, or the cock holding the escape wheel in position, must be bent a trifle to correct the locking. Or, failing this, pivot holes may be drawn and bushed, as already described.

French Dead-beat Escapement

The French steel pallet dead-beat escapement sometimes

seen in marble and other clocks is shown by Fig. 43. It calls for very little special explanation. Wear must be buffed out on the impulse faces only, and as in these escapements very few teeth are embraced by the pallets, setting the pallets nearer to the escape wheel will cause it to lock

properly. The front pallet pivot hole is in a brass eccentric disc, and can be turned with a screwdriver to adjust the depth of the pallets and escape wheel. When the pallets span more teeth or a larger part of the wheel, as in English regulators, setting the pallets nearer to the wheel alters the drop, and makes it unequal without making the teeth lock better.

Fig. 43.—French Dead-beat Escapement.

French "Tictac" Escapement

This is found in French brass drum clocks with little pendulums about 3 in. long, fortunately not made now. The face of one pallet is circular, as from the pallet staff, consequently there is no impulse on it, the escape-wheel tooth resting "dead" on it, until it drops on the other, which is the single impulse pallet. This arrangement wastes power, and consequently the clocks continually stop, especially when they get a little old, as all now are. Some clock repairers try to alter the pallets by giving the entrance or "dead" pallet a little impulse, and bringing the pallets nearer to the escape wheel to equalize the drop. But this is not a very satisfactory procedure. A better way is to make a new pair of recoil pallets embracing three more teeth. The clocks then go; but they are poor timekeepers.

Some repairers convert these clocks by taking away the pallets and pendulum, and fitting on a platform with a cylinder or lever escapement. But when the cost of this and the labour is counted, also the cost of an extra wheel in the train instead of the old escape wheel, it will be found that a new and better clock can be bought for the money, and the old one discarded or used up as material for repairing.

Pin-pallet Dead-beat Escapement

The best known of this type is the French "visible" escapement often seen in front of the dial in marble clocks of good quality. Fig. 44 shows the escapement. The wheel teeth on the fronts, or acting parts, are straight. Their backs are curved to points to clear the pallets, and have as little drop as possible. The pallet arms are usually of brass, and the pin pallets are round, either driven in tight or cemented in with shellac. When driven in they are made of steel; when cemented, agates are used. The round pins are cut away to half, making them D-shaped, having the curved parts as impulse faces and the straight parts as backs. The straight parts should point exactly to the centre of the escape wheel, and the pins

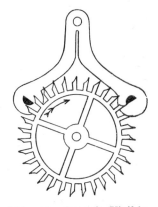

Fig. 44.—French Visible Escapement.

should be a little less in full diameter than the space between two teeth points. The pallets should also be set exactly upright in their holes.

"Drop."—This escapement is a puzzle to many inexperienced workmen, but is really simple when its underlying principles have once been mastered. The teeth points should fall exactly on the pin centres when they "drop"; then as the pallet continues its motion towards the centre of the escape wheel it slides down the straight front of the tooth, and causes no recoil of the wheel or other movement. In impulse, the tooth point slides off the rounded face of the pin, and, leaving its edge, another tooth drops on to the other pallet. If the teeth fall any farther up, they lock too deeply, and the pallet arms must be separated a little more by bending or by warming and shifting the stone back, until the drop is correct. If the teeth drop on the curved part of the pin that gives the impulse, the locking is not deep enough, and the pallet arms must be closed, or the stone moved towards the wheel.

Then there is the amount of the drop. If there is too much on the entrance pallet, lower the pallets, bringing them closer to the wheel; if too much on the exit pallet, remove the pallets farther from the wheel. If there is not enough drop on either and the pallets just catch on the teeth points, while the locking is quite correct, probably one pallet back does not point exactly to the escape-wheel centre. In any case, one or both pallets want a slight twist round, so as to let the teeth points drop earlier.

In a visible escapement, generally the brass escapement cocks are movable a little, and can be shifted this way or that as required to adjust the distance between the centres of the escape wheel and pallets. In those in which the pallets are between the plates, the front pivot is carried in an eccentric, like recoil French clocks. But the locking can only be regulated by either closing the brass pallet arms by bending, or by warming the shellac and moving the stones away from or towards the wheel.

Worn Pallets.—If the agate pallets become worn or chipped, they can be warmed to soften the shellac and pushed in more or drawn out, to bring the action on a new part. After this, some considerable adjustment on the lines already described is always needed, as since the stones are a slack fit in their holes it is nearly impossible to re-cement them in exactly the same positions as before. Should a stone be broken or lost, a new one may be obtained from a clock-material shop and cemented in.

Worn steel pin pallets are best replaced with new ones. Generally they are, driven in tight, and may be knocked out. New pins must be very carefully made from steel rod, filed flat to size, and hardened, a good polish being put on when finishing.

Bent Teeth.—In French pin-pallet escapements there is very little drop, and the teeth points are thin. This being so, a tooth just a little bent causes the pallets to catch it and the clock to stop. Therefore in examining such an escapement it is not sufficient to try the drop on a few teeth; it must be carefully tested on every tooth of the wheel for a complete revolution, and any faulty teeth straightened.

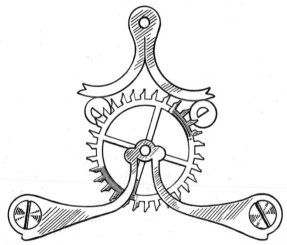

Fig. 45.—Brocot Visible Dead-beat Escapement.

Another form of the French visible dead-beat escapement—the Brocot—is shown by Fig. 45

Other Pin-Pallet Escapements.—A few clocks have pin-pallet escapements in which the impulse planes are on the wheel teeth, and the pallets are small, round hard-steel pins. The teeth must drop on the pins just below the corner, and as little below as possible. The pallets must be closed and brought a little nearer to the wheel.

CHAPTER 10

Strike and Alarm Work

"LOCKING-PLATE" Striking Work.—All striking work has much in common, although the details may differ. The first example to be taken will be the simple striking work to be found in an American dial or a "square" clock, for it is simple and a good example of "locking-plate" striking mechanism.

Fig. 46 shows the striking part of the mechanism. For the sake of simplicity the frame plates are not shown, and some of the wheels are represented by plain circles. A is a wheel mounted upon the same arbor as the main wheel of the striking train. It will be seen that it has twelve slots in it, at distances progressing regularly from one tooth to twelve. This is called the "locking-plate", or "count wheel", and its duty is to determine the number of blows struck by the hammer. The next wheel B is the "pin-wheel", and has around its circumference a number of pins, each of which in turn raises and releases the hammer as the wheel revolves. The pins are so spaced that the distance between each corresponds with a movement of the wheel A equal to *one tooth*. Thus, when A moves through a distance of three teeth, the pins in B strike three blows. The next wheel C is the locking wheel, and its purpose is to effect the stopping of the striking train when the right number of blows has been struck according to the divisions of A. The ratio between wheels B and C is such that C makes one complete turn for every hammer blow struck by B. The next is the "fly" D. Its duty is to regulate the speed of striking, and prevent the train running too fast. It also serves the purpose of a warning wheel on American clocks, though many other forms have their "warning" on another wheel which comes between the locking wheel and the fly.

E represents the centre arbor of the clock, which revolves once an hour and carries the minute hand. In it is a projecting arm F which, as it comes round, raises the lever G, another arm of which raises H, which rests in the slot in the cam fixed on the wheel C and locks the striking train. It is evident that, on G and H being raised, the wheel C will be released and the train will be free to run until the arm I fixed to G comes into contact with the fly or an arm fixed

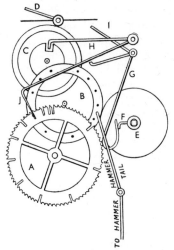

Fig. 46.—American Striking Work.

to it. It thus runs about half a revolution of the fly, which, of course, is not sufficient to strike at all, and is termed the warning. It takes place about five to ten minutes before the hour, and its purpose is to enable the slowly-moving centre arbor of the timekeeping part E to unlock and then to release the striking part at exactly the right moment. The arm on E, continuing to advance, at last lets the levers G and I fall just at the hour. H and J (all one piece) also fall, and I releases the fly, and the striking train commences to run. J, it will be seen, falls upon the wheel A just between two teeth, and H cannot therefore fall into the slot in the cam on C until a deep slot comes round on A and lets J fall into it. Then H falls into the slot and stops C, by which time a number of blows will have been struck by the hammer equal to the number of teeth passed in the wheel A. This entire action should be most carefully studied.

Now for the essential points to be observed in putting together the striking train. First of all, when the arm H

F

stops the train by falling into the slot in the cam on wheel
C, one pin on the pin wheel should have *just struck a blow*
and released the hammer, and the hammer tail must on
no account be in contact with the next pin. If it is so,
there will be a resistance to the starting of the striking
train which will sometimes stop it. If, when it is put
together, this is found to be wrong, the plate must be
lifted and the wheel shifted a tooth or so until corrected.
Secondly, when the striking has stopped, the arm projecting from the fly must be half a revolution or more from
I, so as to have about half a turn at the "warning" before
being stopped by I. This is important.

Now these two points—the freedom of the hammer tail
from the pins in the pin wheel and the "run" at warning
—are common to all striking work.

If the striking does not take place exactly when the
minute hand points to the hour, bend the arm F fixed to
E until it releases lever G at just the right instant. If the
clock strikes more than it ought—two hours together
without any interval—it is because the arm H does not
fall into the slot and is *too high*. The remedy for this is to
bend it down. If the clock only strikes one at each hour,
the arm H is too *low*; bend it up. Sometimes a clock will not
stop striking properly because the side of the slot into
which H falls is worn away and forces H out again. If so,
file it up nice and square, or even undercut it a little Also
see that the point of J falls exactly in the centre of each
slot in the wheel A

This kind of striking, with slight modifications, will be
found in Dutch striking clocks, and will need no further
explanation. Cuckoo clocks, also, are much the same; but,
of course, the double set of wires to the small bellows
makes them somewhat more troublesome to adjust properly
(see Chapter 13).

French Locking-plate Striking Work.—Two distinct
kinds of striking are in use in French clocks. The first,
the "locking-plate" striking, is somewhat similar to the

American striking mechanism. Fig. 47 is a view under the
dial showing the discharging work, and Fig. 48 is a back
view showing the locking-plate.

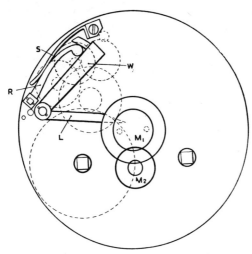

Fig. 47.—Front View of French Locking-plate Strike Work.

Taking Fig. 47 first, M^1 is the cannon or minute-hand
pinion which turns once in an hour. In it are two pins,
opposite each other. These two pins, as they revolve, lift
the end of the lever L every half hour. It will be observed
that French clocks invariably strike the hours and half
hours. The lever L is pivoted upon a stud fixed to the plate
near its edge, and together with the arm W forms one
piece. At the end of the arm W is a projection which goes
through the plate where an oblong slot is cut, and engages
the pin in the warning wheel. This arm effects the warning
in the same manner as in an American clock. The lever R
is fixed to an arbor which goes right across the movement,
and is raised by W at each half hour. To the same arbor
that R is fixed to, there is also an arm which engages with a

pin in the locking wheel, and stops the striking train. The pin wheel is fitted with pins which operate the hammer tail in the same manner as in an American clock.

Turning to Fig. 48, the locking-plate is mounted outside the back plate, upon the extended arbor of the intermediate wheel and turns once in twelve hours.

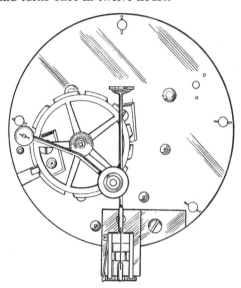

Fig. 48.—Back View of French Striking Work, showing Locking-plate.

Its circumference is spaced out on the same principle as the locking-plate of an American clock, except that the notches are wider than those of American clocks to allow for the single blow which occurs at each half hour. A projecting stud, which is fixed to the arm which locks the striking train, comes through an opening in the back plate and rests upon the edge of the locking-plate. When it is in a notch of the locking-plate, it prevents the locking wheel revolving, but so long as it rests upon a high portion of the locking-plate the locking wheel is free to revolve. The pins in the pin wheel are so arranged that one revolution of the locking wheel is equivalent to one blow of the hammer.

Now see what happens when the clock is about to strike. First of all the striking train is locked by the pin in the locking wheel resting on the locking arm fixed to R, and the projecting stud is in a notch of the locking-plate. The pin in the warning wheel is at the top, and half a revolution from the warning lever w.

As the clock goes on, one of the pins in M^1 (the cannon pinion), lifts the lever L. Immediately, the pin in the locking wheel is released, as the arm R, and consequently the locking arm fixed upon the same arbor, is raised. The striking train then "runs" to the extent of half a turn of the warning wheel, and is arrested by the pin in the warning wheel coming in contact with the projection in the arm w. This is the "warning".

The striking train then pauses until the pin, still advancing, at last passes the point of the lever L, which lever then drops, and, of course, w also. This releases the warning wheel, and the striking runs and continues to do so until the projecting stud drops into the next notch in the locking-plate, when it at once locks the train by coming into contact with the pin in the locking wheel.

At the half hours the same thing occurs, except that as the projecting stud simply falls back into the same notch of the locking-plate, the locking wheel is arrested again after making but one revolution, and therefore having struck one blow. The wider notches in the rim of the locking-plate allow for this.

In putting the clock together, the following points must be observed. When the train is locked by the pin in the locking wheel resting on the locking arm, one blow should just have been struck, and the hammer tail should be quite free and not touching the next pin in the pin wheel. This is imperative. It can be made so by shifting the pin wheel a tooth or so one way or the other. This can usually be done quite easily, for the rear pivot of the arbor runs into "cock" or extra block, fitted to the back plate and secured by a screw. This can easily be taken off to enable the pin-wheel to be adjusted. At the same time, the warning pin must be at least half a revolution from the stop on the arm w to allow for the "run". Shift it until it is so. Should the clock occasionally strike one too many at several of the hours, the locking-plate is probably put on the wrong way of the square it fits on to, and it had better be tried on another way. There is usually a dot on its central bush and on the square. In putting a striking clock together, observe that dots go next to each other. A dot on a wheel is meant to be placed adjoining the marked leaf on the next pinion, and if this rule is observed in putting the striking train together, not much trouble will be experienced in getting it right.

Put a little oil on the pins in the pin wheel, on the warning pin, and on the locking pin in the locking wheel. Oil the pivots of the hammer arbor, and the arbor of R. Do not oil the edge of the locking-plate, or the pivot of the arm L. Put a little on the pins on the cannon pinion.

Should the clock strike not exactly at the hour and half hour, bend the pins on the cannon pinion a trifle in or out as required.

French Rack Striking Work.—French clocks fitted with rack striking are the next form to be considered. Fig. 49 shows the mechanism, which will be seen to be all on the front plate and underneath the dial.

The train is practically the same as before. The pin wheel s, the locking wheel, the warning wheel, and fly are the same in both. In a rack-striking clock the locking wheel is called the "pallet wheel", because its front pivot is prolonged and carries a small "pallet" G whose duty is to "gather" up the rack. In Fig. 49 the gathering pallet is shown affixed to the arbor of the pallet wheel, and close to the rack teeth.

The cannon pinion M^1, the pins, and the levers L and w, are the same as in the locking-plate striking. Also the locking arm pivoted between the plates (shown by a dotted line) is the same, but the lever affixed to it, marked H in Fig. 49, is different, and its purpose is to hold up the rack as the gathering pallet gathers it up tooth by tooth. R is the rack. On the hour wheel which revolves once in twelve hours is the snail O. The latter is a piece of brass shaped to correspond to the different hours to be struck, and determines the distance to which the rack falls at each hour.

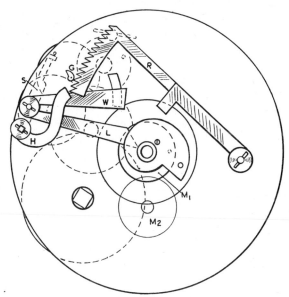

Fig. 49.—Front View of French Rack Striking Work.

How all this mechanism works will now be explained. The striking train is locked by the pin in the pallet wheel resting on the locking arm, and the pin in the warning wheel is half a turn from the stop in the warning lever. As the clock goes, a pin on the cannon pinion M^1 raises the lever L, and also W. A pin projecting from H also raises the rack hook H, and the locking arm with it. The immediate effect of this is to let the rack R fall until the rack-tail falls upon a step of the snail O. Also the locking arm being simultaneously raised, the striking train runs to the extent of half a turn of the warning wheel, until the warning pin falls upon the stop on W. The striking train then pauses until the pin on the cannon pinion passes the tip of the lever L, and lets it fall again. This at once releases the warning wheel, and the train runs.

At each revolution of the pallet wheel, the small gathering pallet G upon its front pivot raises the rack to the extent of one tooth, and a pin of the pin wheel causes one blow to be struck. The rack hook, H, meanwhile rests against the rack teeth, and as soon as the rack is all gathered up it falls to the position shown in Fig. 49. This, of course, brings the locking arm into contact with the pin in the pallet wheel and stops the striking train.

The pin that lets off the half hours is a little nearer to the centre of the cannon pinion, and therefore does not lift the levers L and W and the rack hook H quite so high. It still must lift them high enough to liberate the striking train, but *not high enough to let the rack fall*. The clock, therefore, only strikes one, and the pallet wheel is stopped at the next revolution.

The points to be observed in putting rack striking work together are as follows: as in all striking work, see that the hammer tail is free of the pins in pin wheel, and that the warning wheel has half a turn to "run" when the train is locked. Use the dots on the motion-work wheels as a guide when assembling, and see that the rack-tail on the rack *falls on exactly the right part* of the snail O. The gathering pallet is only pushed on friction tight upon its pivot, and can be pulled off with the pliers. When replacing the gathering pallet see that it is so positioned that it is clear of the rack-teeth when the striking train locks. The best setting is for it to have gathered the last tooth and have moved on about a twelfth of a turn after disengaging with the rack when the striking train locks. This makes certain that it is clear and that the rack can drop freely when released.

Oil the pin-wheel pins, the locking and warning pins, and the pins on the cannon pinion. Do not put any oil on the pivots of the rack or levers L and W, or they may stick.

Should a rack striking clock be found stopped with the tail on the rack jammed against the snail at some time between 12 and 1 o'clock, it shows that for some reason or other the striking work has failed, and the clock still going on has jammed the snail against the tail of the rack. In such a case look for a bent pivot, a want of oil, or a want of endshake somewhere in the striking train. Perhaps the hammer tail is "on the rise"—that is, it is not free of the pins in pin wheel and starting. It may be that the hammer spring is too strong and offers too much resistance to the lifting pins. The gathering pallet may perhaps catch on the points of the rack teeth. A most careful search must be made till the cause of the stoppage is found. When found, it is, as a rule, an easy matter to remedy it.

It may happen that the clock, when put together, only strikes one at each hour. The cause of this is either that the hour pin on the cannon pinion wants bending outwards a little, or that the pin in the lever H requires bending down a trifle. In any case, the lever H must be made to lift a little higher.

A frequent cause of failure in the striking work of French clocks is that the fly is "out of poise", and when hanging with the heavy side downwards when at rest it offers great resistance to starting. The remedy is to poise the fly carefully by bending or filing the thin brass portion.

The striking work of French carriage clocks is merely a modification of the rack striking just described, and the reader will not find much difficulty with it. Some modern English and Continental clocks have a gathering pallet in

Fig. 50.—Movement of a Quarter Chiming and Hour Striking Clock of German Manufacture. The Quarter Chiming is controlled by a Locking-plate, and the Striking by Rack Mechanism. Note the large detachable Sub-plate that carries the Front Pivots of the three Going-barrel Arbors, and the two smaller Plates housing the Winding Gears for the Going and Chiming Trains. The Clock was made by Junghans, of Schramberg

the form of a brass disc with its edge shaped to form a sort of cam. This acts on the rack hook, and gives a silent "gathering" action, without the "click-clack" noise heard with older types. The locking of the striking train is also

Fig. 51.—Back View of German Chiming Clock shown in
Fig. 50.

performed by this gathering pallet, for a step on it locks
against a pin on the rack hook when the latter falls after
the last rack tooth has been gathered.

English "long-case" and bracket clock striking work will
be dealt with in the next chapter.

Chiming Mechanism.—Chiming clocks have become
extremely popular during recent years, and the modern
mass-produced types are very often met with in repair
work. They are fairly simple to deal with, for they are

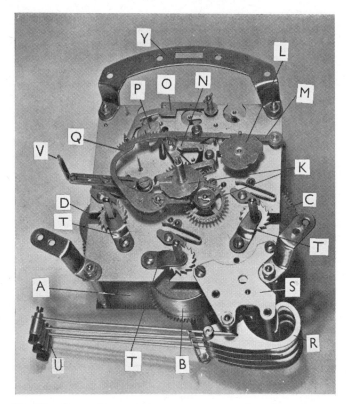

Fig. 52.—Front View of Movement of typical modern under-slung Quarter Chiming Clock. (The Smith "K6A" Movement.)

A—Frame Plates; B—Timekeeping Train Going Barrel; C—Chiming Train Going Barrel; D—Striking Train Going Barrel; K—Motion Work, showing Striking Snail on Hour Wheel; L—Chiming Train Locking-plate; M—Chiming Train Locking Detent; N—Let-off and Warning Detent; O—Rack Hook; P—Gathering Pallet; Q—Striking Rack; R—Hammer-tails, embodying Buffers; S—Sub-frame for Hammers and Chime Barrel; T—Winding Ratchets and Clickworks; U—Hammer Heads; V—"Chime-Silent" lever; Y—Lugs for Attachment to Case.

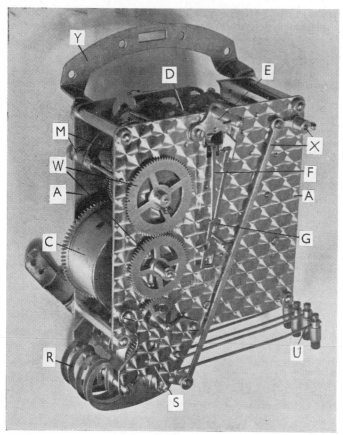

Fig. 53.—Rear View of Movement of typical modern under-slung Quarter Chiming Clock (The Smith "K6A" Movement.)

A—Frame Plates; C—Chiming Train Going Barrel; D—Escapement Pallets; E—Back-cock, or Suspension-cock; F—Crutch; G—Pendulum Rod (with Suspension Spring at top); M—Chiming Train Locking Detent; R—Hammer Tails, embodying Buffers; S—Underslung Sub-frame for Hammers and Chime Barrel; U—Hammer Heads; W—Transmission Wheels Driving Chime Barrel; X—Lifting Rod for Striking Hammers; Y—Lugs for Attachment to Case.

usually fitted with a number of devices designed to make assembly easy.

The chiming train is really just like another striking train, and works on the same principle, except that it is let off every 15 minutes instead of every hour and half-hour. In modern chiming clocks, the chiming train is always controlled by a locking-plate that is mounted on the extended front pivot of the wheel next to the inter-mediate wheel. As the locking-plate is outside the frames, and is secured to the lengthened pivot by one or two set-screws, correct setting is quite easy, for it can be done after the wheelwork is assembled. The locking-plate is usually mounted in front of the front plate, and it is generally arranged to release the striking mechanism at the completion of the chiming of the fourth quarter. This is done either by a pin on the locking-plate, or by a "hump" cam formed on its circumference. This pin or cam lifts a long detent which raises the hook of the striking rack, thus allowing the rack to drop on to the hour snail. At the same time, the detent engages with the warning of the striking train, and so holds the striking until the chimes are completed. As soon as the detent falls into the "fourth quarter" notch in the chiming locking-plate, it releases the striking train.

The rear pivot of the wheel carrying the locking-plate is often extended to carry a wheel that drives the chiming cam barrel, and as this wheel is also secured by set-screws, adjustment to get exactly the right position for the chiming cams is easy. Sometimes there are some intermediate, or "transmission" wheels between the wheel on the extended pivot and that on the cam-barrel, but these are merely for the transmission of the drive. The ratio between the driving wheel on the extended pivot and the driven wheel on the cam-barrel spindle is invariably 1 to 2, the cam-barrel revolving twice during the sounding of the first, second, third and fourth quarters.

The striking train usually raises several of the same

hammers that are lifted by the chiming train, doing so by an arrangement of levers. Sometimes the hammers, which are usually grouped in line on a spindle, are at the back of the clock, but in order to save space, they are often fitted below the rest of the clock mechanism. In this case, they are known as "underslung".

Chiming trains are usually fitted with a self-correcting attachment, which automatically corrects the sequence of the chimes if it should be upset. This may take several forms, but the principle of its action is to lock the train either doubly or more deeply at the conclusion of the chiming of the third quarter. When this has occurred, only the extra long "hour" let-off cam on the cannon pinion can unlock the train, and so the chiming stops until the next hour. This action, of course, effects the correction.

Chiming clocks usually have removable going barrels to all three trains, and are also arranged to allow their hands to be turned backwards. This is done to prevent damage to the mechanism through any careless handling.

Wire Gongs.—Grandfather, French, and many other clocks are often fitted with gongs which consist of a coiled wire. The repairer is sometimes asked to fit a gong of this type, and it is best bought ready-made. The making of clock gongs is a trade to itself, and the reader is not likely to succeed in making a good one at the first attempt. First the wire is brazed into a brass end block, then coiled up into a spiral, and then heated to a bright red evenly all over and hardened. It is next polished, then blued by heat. A gong of round wire is the easiest to make. For a grandfather clock gong, obtain a round steel rod $\frac{3}{16}$ in. thick and 45 in. long. After brazing it to its block, about $1\frac{1}{4}$ in. by $\frac{5}{8}$ in. by $\frac{3}{8}$ in., coil it into a spiral of about three turns and 7 in. outside diameter. To harden the steel, heat it in a forge fire and plunge in water, then polish with fairly quick-cutting emery and finally with the finest. Then blue it in burning charcoal dust or hot sand on an iron plate over a fire. For grandfather clocks, however, a coil of *flat* wire is recommended. A deep-toned hour gong, about 7 in. outer diameter, may be made from flat steel $\frac{3}{16}$ in. wide and $\frac{1}{16}$ in. thick, formed into a spiral of about three complete turns. This will take about 4 ft. 6 in. of wire. The end should be brazed into a slot in a brass block, and the brass block screwed to the gong standard. The quarter gongs may be of wire gradually diminishing to $\frac{1}{8}$ in. wide for the highest note, and thickness in proportion. The diameter may diminish to $4\frac{1}{2}$ in., and the turns from three to two. Several experimental gongs will have to be made to arrive at about the correct notes. The finished gongs can be tuned by shortening from the inner end.

Should a coiled-wire gong be fixed in place of a bell it may fail to give sufficient tone. Generally, the hammer employed to strike the bell of a French clock would be too light to strike a gong, unless the gong was very small. The hammer should be faced with a piece of hard leather, and so adjusted that it is perfectly free of the gong when at rest. See that the gong is fixed perfectly rigid in the metal block, the stalk or gong support being absolutely tight at both ends. The bottom end is screwed with an adjustable nut to the sounding board, and the latter, it is obvious, must be quite firm on its resting place. The gong and support must be free from any other object.

Rod-Gongs.—Most modern quarter-chiming clocks use "rod-gongs", which consist of lengths of rod of circular section, mounted very firmly in screws which are screwed home very tightly into a cast-iron gong-block. For the smaller rod-gongs used for mantel clocks, the material used for the rods is usually bronze, or phosphor-bronze, but for the longer gongs that are fitted to "grandmother" or long-case clocks, steel is often employed.

As the rods are tapered down near to the point where they are inserted in their screws, these gongs are rather frail, and must be handled with care. If they are found to be bent, they must be straightened very cautiously, for they are easily broken.

If it is necessary to remove a gong from its block, the block should be securely gripped in a vice, and the gong-screw should be slackened by a stout screwdriver whose blade is a good fit to the slot in the screw-head. The same precautions must be taken when replacing the gong.

The note of the gong is determined by its length, and when a new gong has to be fitted, the replacement should be slightly longer than is necessary. The note will then be of slightly lower pitch than the proper note, and can be tuned by reducing its length. Cut off the metal at the tip, little by little, and make the final adjustment by careful filing. If the note is accidentally made too high, it can be lowered by further reducing the tapered portion near the screw, but as this weakens the gong, it should be avoided if possible.

Always screw rod-gongs into their block as tightly as possible, and also screw the fixing screws of the block as tight as they will go. A little oil or grease on the threads and under the heads is a help here.

Alarm Mechanism. — The most common kind of alarm clock is perhaps the metal-cased alarm. In putting together an alarm clock, after putting on the hour and minute hands, turn them round carefully and note the exact time the alarm goes off. If this is at, say, 6.30, put the alarm hand on at exactly that hour and it will then be right, and wherever it is set will indicate the correct time of the alarm. Many alarm clocks have "stopwork" to the alarm spring (see Fig. 54). This is to stop the alarm when it has run for a certain distance and prevent its starting again after it has once

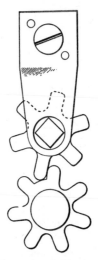

Fig. 54.—A Typical Stopwork.

G

Fig. 55.—Back View of typical Alarm Clock Movement. Made by Smith's English Clocks Ltd.

A—Frame Plates; B—Main Wheel of Time Train; C—Centre Wheel and Pinion; D—Third Wheel; E—Fourth Wheel; F—Pivot Hole of Escape Wheel; G—Lever; H—Balance and Balance Spring; J—Regulator Index; K—Main Wheel of Alarm Train; L—Alarm Escape Wheel; M—Alarm Hammer; N—Alarm Silencing Detent; O—Bell; P—Alarm Setting Spindle; R—Dial Backing Plate (or "False Plate").

stopped. To adjust the stopwork, wind up the spring all but half a turn, and put on the star wheel in such a position that it can be wound no further. It will then allow some six turns of the mainspring to unwind themselves and again bring it to a stop.

Some other types of alarm clocks, such as the "Smith Victory", have a rather different form of "stopwork",

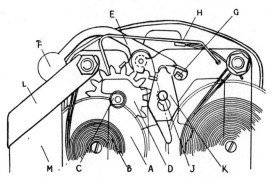

**Fig. 56.—Diagram of the Alarm Mechanism
of a Smith Spring-driven Alarm Clock.**

A—Alarm Train Main Wheel; B—Alarm Mainspring; C—Alarm Escape
Wheel Pinion; D—Alarm Escape Wheel; E—Alarm Pallets and Hammer
Lever; F—Hammer Head; G—Release Spring (tip only); H—Silencing
Detent and Spring; J—Setting Arbor; K—Setting Arbor Friction Spring;
L—Bell-strap; M—Bell.

for the alarm hammer spindle carries an extra rod or
finger, and the mainspring, as it unwinds, touches this, and
so limits the movement of the hammer spindle, eventually
bringing it to a stop.

In older types of clock the alarm bell is often placed on
the top of the clock, and the hammer stem comes through
a slot in the case. In some modern alarm clocks, the bell
is fitted inside the case, or it may even be attached to the
clock movement itself. (Figs. 55 and 56).

The mechanism is very simple, being made up by a
second small mainspring, driving the alarm-train main-
wheel, one intermediate wheel (not always fitted), and a
kind of recoil escapement, somewhat similar to that found
in an American pendulum timepiece. To the pallets is
fixed the hammer stem, which vibrates backwards and
forwards as the train runs down. Fig. 56 shows the
alarm train and explains itself. The essential part of the
arrangement is the mechanism for letting the alarm train
run down at the right moment.

To accomplish this it will be seen that there is a spindle running right through the clock from back to front, with a hand fixed to it which points to the hours on a small dial. Riding loose upon this spindle is an alarm-release wheel, driven from the ordinary "motion-work" which operates the hands, and which revolves once in twelve hours. A projecting boss on this wheel has a kind of cam cut upon it which rests against a pin fixed in the spindle. This is so arranged that once in every twelve hours, as the wheel and cam revolve against the fixed pin, the latter allows the wheel to rise, and a spring beneath it forces it up, and by a catch liberates the alarm train.

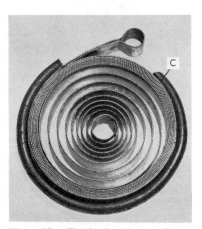

Fig. 57.—Typical Alarm Clock Mainspring shown in Cramp (C).

It is evident that the time of rising of the cam, and consequent discharge of the alarm train, depend on the position of the fixed pin in the spindle, and as the spindle and pin can be revolved by the hand from the back of the clock and set in any position desired, the hand will show the hour when the alarm will go off.

The alarm work found in French drum and carriage clocks is merely a modification of that in ordinary alarm clocks just described.

CHAPTER 11

Cleaning Grandfather Striking Clocks

PHOTOGRAPHS of the movement of a grandfather striking clock are presented by Figs. 58 to 61, whilst Fig. 62 is a diagram of a typical movement of the same general kind, the dial having been removed, and shows the usual arrangement of the striking mechanism. Fig. 62 is a key to the train of wheels between the plates, which wheels cannot be shown in the other diagram.

The Sequence of Operations.—When cleaning the clock, before taking anything apart, place the movement with the dial removed, as in Fig. 59, in its case with the hands on and turn them round, causing the clock to strike. Notice exactly what happens, and from it observe how to put the parts together again. On turning the minute hand, as the hour is approached a pin in the minute wheel M^1 (Fig. 62) lifts the tail end of the warning lever L, which in turn lifts the rack hook C. The rack is thus liberated and falls until its tail

Fig. 58.—Dial of typical Grandfather Clock showing Date Wheel.

Fig. 59.—Front View of typical English "Long-case" hour Striking Movement. (Usually called a "Grandfather" Clock.)

A—Frame Plates; B—Frame Pillars; C—Timekeeping, or "Going" Train Main-wheel; D—Barrel; E—Winding Ratchet Wheel (on end of Barrel); F—Winding Pawl (or "Click") and Spring; G—Minute Wheel and Pinion, carrying Let-off Pin; H—Warning Detent; J—Hour Wheel; K—Going Train Winding Square; L—Striking Train Winding Square; M—Rack Tail; N—12-stepped Striking Snail (the pin on it is to operate the Date Wheel on the Dial); O—Striking Rack; P—Rack Hook; Q—Gathering Pallet; R—Striking Hammer; S—Bell; T—Bell Stud; U—Seat Board.

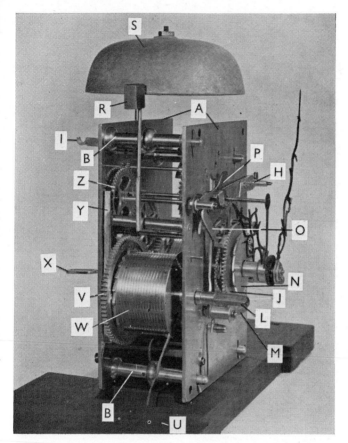

Fig. 60.—Three-quarter View of typical English "Long-case" Hour Striking Movement.

A—Frame Plates; B—Frame Pillars; H—Warning Detent; I—Back Cock; J—Hour Wheel; L—Striking Train Winding Square; M—Rack Tail; N—12-stepped Striking Snail; O—Striking Rack; P—Rack Hook; R—Striking Hammer; S—Bell; U—Seat-board; V—Striking Train Main Wheel; W—Striking Train Barrel; X—Crutch (on Pallet Staff); Y—Hammer Spring; Z—Gathering Pallet Wheel.

Fig. 61.—Back View of typical English "Long-case" Hour Striking Clock Movement.

A—Frame Plates; B—Frame Pillars; C—Timekeeping Train Main-wheel; R—Striking Hammer; S—Bell; T—Bell Stud; U—Seat-board. V—Striking Train Main-wheel; W—Striking Train Barrel; X—Crutch.

rests against one of the steps of the snail o. The depth of these steps regulates the number of blows struck at each hour. Before the rack fell, the running of the striking train of wheels was prevented by the gathering-pallet resting upon a stop pin in the rack. But when the rack falls the gathering-pallet is released and the train runs until a pin in the warning wheel catches against a stop block attached to the warning lever. This run is called the warning, and takes place a few minutes before the hour. The minute hand continues to advance, the pin in the minute wheel passes the end of the warning lever, and at the hour the lever falls again and liberates the warning wheel. The striking train then runs, and at each revolution of the pallet wheel the gathering-pallet gathers up one tooth of the rack and a pin in the pin wheel causes one blow to be struck. Continuing to run and strike, the rack is at last all gathered up and the gathering-pallet once more comes to rest against the stop pin in the rack. This action should be studied closely until the function of each part is thoroughly understood.

Taking Movement Apart.—To take the movement to pieces, first take out the pallet and the crutch. Then remove the rack, hour wheel, warning lever, rack hook, gathering-pallet, minute wheel, and cannon pinion, in the order named. Take off the bell and bell standard, and take the plates apart.

Cleaning.—With a stiff brush like a tooth-brush bearing powdered rottenstone and oil mixed to a paste, scrub the plates up and down in straight lines until they are bright. Similarly scrub the wheels and all other brass parts. Then pour some petrol or benzoline into a basin, and with a very clean brush thoroughly wash the rottenstone and oil from all parts, and dry with a clean cloth. With pointed wooden pegs clean out the spaces between the pinion leaves, and peg out the pivot holes in the plates until they are quite clean inside. Brush out the wheel teeth thoroughly clean.

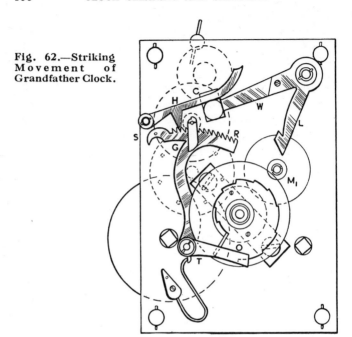

Fig. 62.—Striking
Movement   of
Grandfather Clock.

Reassembling.—The movement may now be put
together again, a little oil being given to the clicks and
click springs on the barrels. When the bell hammer and
all the wheels are between the plates and in place, try each
to see whether the pivots have much side play in the pivot
holes. The most important wheel is the escape wheel. If
its pivot holes are very wide, they must be bushed, as
described on an earlier page.

Then put on the minute wheel, rack, rack-hook, warning
lever, and gathering-pallet temporarily, to see that the
striking train wheels are in correctly.

To test them proceed as follows: Wind up the striking
barrel about a turn and give the gut a twist round the
fingers. Then, pulling on the gut, cause the rack to fall

a few teeth and let the pallet gather it up slowly. Observe how the train stops when the gathering-pallet stops against the rack pin. It should do this immediately after the last blow is struck, so that when the train is at rest the hammer tail is quite free of the lifting pins in the pin wheel. If it stops with a pin against the hammer-tail, it is wrong. Shift the gathering-pallet to another square, and try it on all four sides until one is found that is right. If none seems right, but a midway position seems to be required, the top plate of the frame must be gently lifted up and the pin wheel turned one tooth in the pallet-wheel pinion. Then try again, and finally pin on the gathering-pallet.

Next see whether the warning is correct. When the striking train stops, the pin in the warning wheel should not be close to the stop block on the warning lever, but should have a run of at least a quarter of a turn before coming to it. If too close, the plate must be raised and the teeth of the pallet-wheel shifted in the warning-wheel pinion. These are the two points that must be attended to in any striking clock.

Next oil the front pivot holes with good clock oil, and put on the cannon pinion. Do not forget the flat brass spring under the cannon pinion. Put the minute hand on it and turn it round to see when it strikes. See that when the warning lever falls the minute hand points exactly to the hour; the teeth of the cannon pinion can be shifted in the minute wheel to adjust this. Then pin on the rack, rack hook, warning lever, etc., and put the hour wheel and snail on in such a position that the rack tail falls in the centre of a step at the hour. This can be regulated by shifting the teeth in the minute pinion. Oil the lifting pins in the pin wheel, the hammer spring where it touches the hammer, the rack spring where it touches the rack, the stop pin in the rack, the warning pin in the warning wheel, and the lifting pin in the minute wheel. Also oil the back pivots. Then clean the pallets with petrol, and the crutch in which the pendulum-rod goes. If the pallets are in fair condition, put them in place and oil them and their pivots, also the slot in the crutch. If they are very badly worn, it will be best to buff out the ruts with an emery-stick, or face them with watch mainspring as described earlier. Then try the pallets in the clock, and if necessary trim off the points with a file until the wheel moves through satisfactorily without catching.

The dial can next be put on and the clock started. If after going a little while the pallets catch upon the points of the escape-wheel teeth, reduce the offending point a little by filing the pallet. See that the pendulum-rod is not sticky where it passes through the crutch, and give it a little oil there.

Getting Clock into Beat.—Let the clock be exactly in beat. To test this, bring the pendulum to rest and mark the back of the case with a pencil behind the bottom of the rod. Draw the pendulum to one side until it ticks, mark the point, then draw it to the other side and mark that point. If the clock is in beat, these two marks will be equidistant from the central point. If unequal, bend the wire crutch to the "narrow" side and note the result. Work in this way until correct. See that the hands are quite free from each other, the dial, and the glass. See that the lines wind up straight upon the barrels to the top, and that they are not long enough to allow the weights when run down to touch the floor, or the lines may twist up.

Moon Disc of Grandfather Clock.—The moon disc has usually two moons painted upon it and revolves once in two months. Only one half of the disc is visible at one time. In all cases the discs are worked from the motion work. The hour wheel that carries the snail is the only wheel that moves slowly enough for the purpose, and motion is communicated from this upwards through either one or two gear wheels, the last of which moves the moon disc one tooth per day or one tooth each twelve hours. When the moon disc moves one tooth per day it has 58 teeth; when it moves one tooth each twelve hours it has 116 teeth.

The moon disc itself cannot reach the hour wheel on account of the second pivot between. The method of moving it varies. Sometimes an idle wheel is pivoted on a pipe through which the seconds pivot passes. This wheel runs with the hour wheel and turns once in twelve hours. A projecting pin in it moves the moon disc. The disc is sometimes moved by a lever and "jumper", actuated by the pin in the hour wheel itself; but if all parts are missing, the first method is the easier to supply. The idle wheel should have as many teeth as the wheel on the snail that drives it. The figures on the half-circle, 1 to $29\frac{1}{2}$, are for showing the moon's age. There will be no hand, the moon itself pointing to the figure showing its age. A small brass pipe, something like the pipe and bridge on which the hour wheel revolves, can be made to pass over the seconds pivot and the idle wheel run on it.

CHAPTER 12

Cleaning and Repairing Pin-pallet Lever Clocks

THE type of portable clock most frequently met with is the familiar nickel-plated or enamelled drum clock of British or Continental manufacture, the movement of which is shown in Fig. 63. The movement, on the whole, is similar to that of the cheap pendulum clock described in Chapters 1 and 6, and it is cleaned and repaired in much the same manner. But, of course, the escapement is different.

To take a drum clock movement out of its case, unscrew and remove the two feet and take out a small screw or screws found at the top of the case, and the entire movement will then come out from the back. Before doing this, the winding keys, etc., must be taken off by unscrewing in the reverse direction to that of winding, and the set-hands knob pulled off. This liberates the back.

The common form of pin-pallet lever escapement is shown in Fig. 64. Attached to the balance which spins freely between pivots is a hair-spring which causes the balance, when given an impulse, to vibrate backwards and forwards. The escape wheel and pallets are of the dead-beat form, very similar to an alarm-clock escapement. Instead of a crutch being attached to the pallets to work with a pendulum, there is a lever. At one end of this is a fork to give impulse to the balance through an "impulse pin". At the other end of the lever is a counterpoise to balance it. The impulse pin is set upright in the centre boss of the balance, and as it comes round enters the centre notch of the lever fork. This moves the lever a little, unlocking an escape-wheel tooth, and allowing it to give impulse. This impulse is transmitted by the lever to the impulse pin, and thus the balance receives a little push onwards. The balance, continuing its motion, is at last

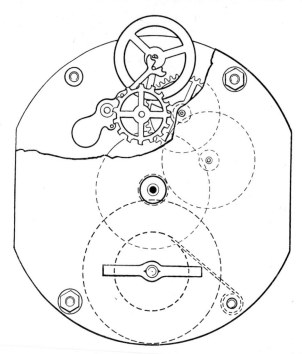

Fig. 63.—Lay-out of typical Pin-pallet Lever Timepiece.

brought to rest, and the hairspring causes it to return. The impulse pin enters the centre notch of the lever fork, unlocks a tooth, and the lever gets another impulse, and so on.

Between the impulses the escape-wheel teeth are locked, exactly as in the English dead-beat escapement, and the pallets and lever do not move. The balance, also, is quite free to spin, the lever not touching it. The staff of the balance has a slot cut on it opposite the impulse pin, to allow the prongs of the lever fork to pass. The use of the outer prongs of the lever is to prevent the lever moving and unlocking the escape-wheel teeth between impulses.

Fig. 64 shows what is meant, and represents the lever fork and the balance axis between two impulses. If the lever gets a shake or from some accidental cause comes against the balance axis, the prong will rest against the axis, and the lever can get no farther until the impulse pin comes round and enters the centre notch, by which time the slot on the balance axis will be in the proper position to allow the lever fork to pass.

In this escapement there are two depths or actions that must be adjusted correctly. The first is the pallet depth or action between the escape-wheel teeth and pallets, and should be adjusted to "lock" in the same way. The second is the lever depth or action between the lever fork and the balance axis and impulse pin. The lever must have sufficient motion between its banking pins for the horn or prong to be quite free of the axis of the balance and have some shake. To test this, hold the balance with the finger, half a turn round. Then place a finger-tip or pair of tweezers on the lever counterpoise, and try the "shake" of the prong against the balance axis. Let the balance come round, and hold it on the other side, trying the shake of the other prong in the same way. If they touch and have no shake, the balance cannot vibrate freely. If the points of the lever prongs can pass the balance axis and seem too short, lengthen the lever by straightening up the bend in it a little.

In these clocks the balances must be adjusted in their bearings so as to be quite free and have the least trifle of endshake; but on no account must they rock about. It is very important that the points or pivots of the balance are central, true, and sharp. Sometimes they merely wear blunt or rounded; at others they wear all on one side.

The hairspring (not shown in Fig. 64) is an important part of the escapement. It is passed at its outer end through a hole in a brass stud, and held in place by a tapered pin. The outer coil then passes through a wire loop or between two pins, which are set in the regulator. These pins are set on the lever which can be seen in front of F in Fig. 3. The spring should pass freely between these pins, and when the balance is at rest should stand between them, not touching either. Then when the clock is going the spring will play evenly between them. The hairspring should also lie flat in the clock.

If properly "in beat", when the balance is at rest the impulse pin will be in the lever fork, and the balance axis, impulse pin, and pallet axis will be in a straight line.

If one of these clocks gains while the regulator is at "slow", and the hairspring is quite free between the regulator pins, it may be made to go a little slower (up to five minutes per day) by bending the pins wider apart and giving the spring more play between them. If the alteration required is more than this, the spring must be unpinned, and the centre brass collet turned round on the balance axis, so that when again pinned in and in beat the hairspring

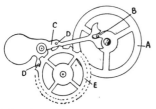

Fig. 64.—Pin-pallet Escapement of Smith Spring-driven Alarm Clock.

A—Balance wheel; B—Impulse Pin; C—Lever; D—Pallet-pins; E—Escape-wheel.

is longer. If such a clock loses, the reverse process can be followed, closing the regulator pins a little for a small alteration, and shortening the hairspring for a larger one.

Before making any such alteration, see if the clock is clean and oiled properly, as a dirty clock or sticky oil will cause all sorts of errors.

The parts requiring oil are the balance pivots and escape wheel and lever pivots, and the pallet pins. The regulator pins must be perfectly clean and dry; also the hairspring where it passes between them, or else they will become sticky, giving the spring a jerky action and causing the clock to gain.

Different varieties of this escapement are met with;

H

but the principle of all is the same, and if the action of the usual form of escapement is mastered, no difficulty will be found with its varieties as seen in clocks by different makers.

The timekeeping train of an alarm clock is usually fitted with a pin-pallet lever escapement—in fact, an alarm clock is just a pin-pallet timepiece with an alarm train and a release mechanism added on. For this reason, the contents of this chapter apply to the timekeeping mechanism of an alarm clock.

The escapements of cylinder drum clocks, French lever carriage clocks, etc., come under the head of watchwork, and need an expert watchmaker to clean and repair them properly. As already stated, a clock with pin-pallet lever escapement is really a big and comparatively coarsely made watch.

CHAPTER 13

Cleaning and Repairing Cuckoo Clocks

IN cuckoo clocks, the cuckoo is mounted upon a wire arm, which, as the clock begins to strike, swings forward and pushes open the little door, the bird just projecting. The door is linked to the wire carrying arm by a length of wire, and on the completion of striking the arm draws the door shut again. A projecting wire upon the top of one of the little bellows at each blow raises the cuckoo's tail, making the bird "bow" to the audience, and by little internal wires, to which the wings and beak are jointed, the "bowing" simultaneously opens the wings and beak.

A cuckoo clock is a most difficult clock to clean properly; indeed, valuable cuckoo clocks have been entirely spoiled by having been tampered with by inexperienced persons. Start by drawing out the pin and then unscrew the brass nut that holds the hands; remove these, then the four pins that hold the dial in place, and the two doors, and draw out the wire nails holding the back to the movement. This will then be clear, and the small door that the bird comes out of being removed, the works should be well studied. Note how the bird is sent out and how the tilting motion is given to cause its mouth to open and its wings to spread. The slender wire fixed to the left-hand bellows does this, and a lever near the bottom of the rod on which the bird is fixed causes it to go out, calling "cuc" "koo", and then allows it to return. A rough sketch of the various parts will help in putting the whole together, because, unless the five lever bars at the left-hand side are in their proper places, it will all be out of order. The lowest bar has a wire upright which lifts the right-hand bellows, the next

115

lifts the other bellows, and the bar above is the hammer to strike the gong which accompanies the bird's calls. Another lever counts on the count-wheel the number to be called, etc. The difficulty lies in this mechanism, but after study it may be managed. Use a thin piece of card to clean out the dust which will have accumulated in the cap part opposite the lips of the pipes.

The going part is like that of all other clocks, and so need cause no trouble. Replace the chains, then fix on the back with the gong attached and the dial, making the hands agree with the hour struck, and replace the small door on the front part with wire attached to the pedestal of the bird. Oil all the pivot holes, giving a drop to each and to the tips of the bars and each pallet, and one drop to the clutch where the pendulum works in the loop.

Should a cuckoo clock, after going a short time, begin to strike in advance of the right hour, it may be that the stopping mechanism is defective. Observe carefully the thin bent wire that dips into the slots of the count-wheel and regulates the number of blows struck. See that it falls clear and well into the slots, and that when it does so the inner part of the same arm locks the striking train properly. When the parts are running fast it is difficult to see just what happens, but by placing a finger on the fly and letting it turn only half a turn at a time, the action can be watched.

In a case in which a clock regularly strikes one hour in advance, proceed as follows: If the hour hand is capable of being turned to a fresh position, simply turn it until it points to the hour struck. If not, lift the striking hook at the back of the clock, or open one side and raise the warning lever. In this way the clock may be struck round without moving the hands until the hour struck and the hands correspond.

Making "Cuckoo" Mechanism.—This mechanism may be bought of material dealers; or the reader may attempt to make it for himself. Two pipes are required, these being in reality small organ pipes, placed not mouth downwards, as in an organ, but mouth upwards, one at each side of the case. An opening is cut in the side of the clockcase to improve the clearness of the note. The pipes may be made of cigar-box wood, but the tone is better if white pine is used. Dress a board up to the thickness of a cigar-box lid, about 1 ft. square. Make it perfectly smooth and true; then cut it into four lengths 1 in. wide and four lengths $\frac{3}{4}$ in. wide, four being $6\frac{1}{2}$ in. long and four 7 in. long. The $6\frac{1}{2}$-in. set is for the pipe to call "cuc", and the 7-in. set for the one to call "koo". Then proceed to make the lips. Take two of the broad pieces and mark, exactly $\frac{1}{2}$ in. from their ends, a cross-line, and $\frac{1}{4}$ in. from that mark another cross-line. With a sharp chisel cut out the space between the lines, leaving uncut at each side the thickness of the side-pieces, which will be glued to it. Now carefully cut the lip—that is, the part that has to speak—of each one. Begin by making a sloping cut $\frac{5}{8}$ in. above this opening, dressing it down carefully to a uniform thickness at the opening, and reducing it to the thickness of an ordinary thin postcard. To the other give a little longer slope, this being for the large 7-in. pipe.

Make up the pipes by placing the two wide pieces that are uncut on the bench, and glue two of the narrow pieces on the edges, placing them edgewise upon the bottom pieces. Then place the two pieces with the lips cut, and glue the edges; clamp both up square, or place weights upon them. When dry, run thin glue down inside each seam, so that there will be no air-holes, or the pipes will have a poor sound. Cut the blocks to fit the ends where the lips have been cut, no longer than is necessary to reach the opening facing the lip. Before gluing it in position, shave a thin piece off the upper part of the wind passage, taking a little more off at the entrance where the bellows are to be placed; or cut away the lower portion of the piece that was cut for the lip, and fix a small partly hollowed piece for the cap, thus leaving the blocks flush with the side pieces; the opening between this block and the cap should be made so as to admit a piece of thin postcard. This amount of wind is quite sufficient. Fix the small bellows to the small pipe, and the larger bellows to the other. The air passage is at the thin end of the bellows and down the open space at the blocked end of the pipe. Glue triangular pieces from the pipe under the bellows to support them, and place a thin piece of lead upon the top right weight to sound the "cuc" "koo" quickly. The top lid of each bellows has a small eyelet in front, to which should be fixed an S-shaped wire to lift them alternately. One wire is $\frac{3}{4}$ in. longer, to be clear of the other when rising. Attach the other ends to the two levers, which are lifted by the pin-wheel of the clock. The bellows are $2\frac{1}{2}$ in. by $1\frac{1}{2}$ in., and are of kid. Try the pipes with the bellows before gluing to the case. The large bellows are placed on the going side of the clock, the smaller on the striking side. Be sure that the small one lifts first, to call "cuc".

CHAPTER 14

Cleaning Regulator Clocks

A REGULATOR is understood to be a clock made especially to show a very close rate of timekeeping—a watchmaker's clock on which he relies to regulate his watches and clocks. It should be furnished with a weight as motive power, also a one-second pendulum, a seconds hand, a dead-beat or other escapement with similar accuracies, and acting surfaces made to reduce friction to its minimum. There is no law to prevent any person from making or selling any timekeeper marked "regulator", any more than there is of selling a watch stamped "accurate" or "perfect timekeeper". A perfect timekeeper has not yet been produced, but a "regulator" is an acknowledged standard quality.

Next to an English one-second pendulum regulator, the Vienna regulator is one of the best timekeepers to be had. Its great advantage lies in the possession of a long and fairly heavy pendulum and a carefully made dead-beat escapement. It is driven by a weight, which is superior to a spring, in that the power does not vary when wound up fully or nearly run down, but is always the same.

On an earlier page, the special form of pallets used in the dead-beat escapement is illustrated and described, and the adjustment of the escapement is explained. The resting surfaces of the pallets, or their "locking faces", as clockmakers would say, are struck from the pallet pivots as a centre, and consequently the escape-wheel teeth, when resting upon them, neither advance nor recoil, but move only when they give impulse across the faces of the pallets. This form of escapement, invented by Graham, is admitted to be the best yet intro-

**Fig. 65.—Front View of Movement of English "Regulator"
Timepiece with Compensated Pendulum.**

A—Frame Plates; B—Frame pillars; C—Main-wheel; D—Maintaining
Power Ratchet Wheel; E—Maintaining Power Ratchet-click Arbor;
F—Barrel, with Winding Ratchet on far end; G—Winding Click; H—
Cannon Pinion (on extended Centre-wheel Arbor); I—Set-hands Friction
Spring; J—Minute Wheel and Pinion; K—Minute Wheel Cock; L—Hour
Wheel; M—Hour Wheel Cock; N—Cock for Front Pallet Arbor Pivot;
O—Escape Wheel Pivot, lengthened to carry Seconds Hand; P—Pendulum
Suspension Bracket; Q—Upper Rating Nut on Suspension Spring Support;
R—Trunnion Adjustment Screw; S—Beat Setting Adjustment; T—Rods
of "Gridiron" Compensation of Pendulum; U—Seat-board; V—Holding-
down Screws for Movement.

Fig. 66.—Three-quarter Front View of English "Regulator" Clock.

A—Frame Plates; B—Frame Pillars; F—Barrel, with Winding Ratchet on far end; H—Cannon Pinion (on Extended Centre-wheel Arbor); J—Minute Wheel and Pinion; K—Minute Wheel Cock; L—Hour Wheel; M—Hour Wheel Cock; N—Cock for Front Pallet Pivot; O—Escape Wheel Front Pivot, lengthened to carry Seconds Hand; P—Pendulum Suspension Bracket; Q—Upper Rating Nut on Suspension Spring Support; R—Trunnion Adjustment Screw; S—Beat Setting Adjustment; T—Rods of "Gridiron" Compensation of Pendulum; U—Seat-board; V—Holding down Screw for Movement.

duced for ordinary clocks; its only superior is the "Gravity", used in turret clocks and sometimes in the best regulators. As already pointed out, Vienna regulators are generally

well made, have light wheels and small pivots, and are
driven by a comparatively light weight; thus, as there is no
excessive driving force, they need to be kept clean and
well oiled.

"Maintaining Work."—It will be observed that there is
"maintaining work" to keep the clock going while it is
being wound. In most spring clocks this is unnecessary,
but in a weight clock, unless some such arrangement were
provided, the act of winding would not only stop the
clock for the minute or so occupied in winding, but would
cause the escape wheel to travel backwards and double
the error. A careful examination of the barrel and main
wheel will amply repay the worker. It will be seen that a
ratchet and curved spring are interposed, and it is through
this spring that the driving power reaches the clock. A
pawl, or "detent", as it is called, falls by its own weight
into the ratchet teeth, and, when the clock is being wound,
prevents the ratchet and curved spring from being carried
backwards; the curved spring in the meantime keeps the
clock going until winding is completed.

Removing Movement.—To remove the movement of a
Vienna regulator, undo the two set-screws just underneath
the clock and draw the movement forwards. The pendulum
will be let in the case and need not be disturbed. Hands
and dial must come off as usual. The plates and wheels,
etc., must be polished with rottenstone and cleaned in the
ordinary way. Repairs of any kind are seldom needed.
The gut line, if broken, is easily replaced with a violin
"A" string, purchased at a music-seller's, the method of
replacement being self-evident.

Setting Up.—To set up a Vienna regulator, proceed as
follows: first hang it upon a stout picture-nail, and adjust
for upright by means of the pendulum and the enamelled
scale at the bottom of the case, the pendulum when at
rest just indicating zero on the scale. Then screw the two
steadying screws, one each side of the bottom of the case,
firmly into the wall. Finally, set in beat by means of the

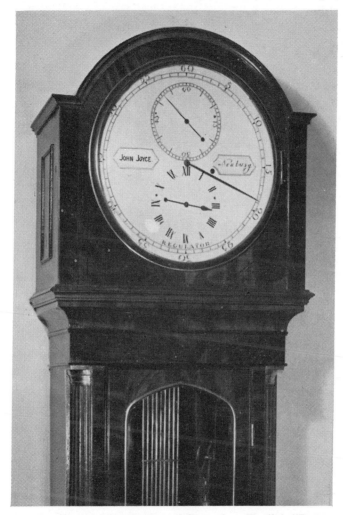

Fig. 67.—Dial and Upper Part of Case of an English "Regulator" Timepiece.

adjusting screw on the crutch, which can be easily manipulated without disturbing anything. In most clocks of this type, the "seconds" hand revolves once in about forty seconds.

Vienna Regulator Gaining.—If the hands move too easily, it will account for serious irregularities, or if the escape-wheel teeth do not lock properly on the pallets the clock will gain. To test this, take out the movement and, having "set up" the maintaining work, move the crutch slowly across so as to allow a tooth to "drop" on to one of the pallets. Observe the pallet carefully, and see that the tooth point falls on the circular locking face, close to the pallet corner. If it falls beyond the corner and on to the inclined face direct, the pallet must be advanced until correct. The teeth should fall on the locking faces as near to the corner as possible; the merest hair's breadth is sufficient margin. Too much will stop the clock. The writer has known a fine spider's web spun from the pendulum rod to the case back behind the movement cause one of these clocks to gain many minutes in the course of each day.

Regulator Striking Clock.—Many forms of clock are marked "regulator", and some are of cheap manufacture. Generally a regulator is a non-striker of the highest-class manufacture made to record very close time. However, some regulators are met with that have rack striking work, resembling that of a grandfather clock, and on this principle most others are made.

Move the minute hand slowly to the hour to test the warning and striking, and make a note of any part that requires correcting or repairing, as the clock is taken to pieces. A clock that stops in the going is seldom wrong in the striking work. The striking part should be examined before taking the plates apart. Move the pin round slowly until it engages the lifting piece, and notice the action of the latter with its contact to the rack hook and warning piece. As soon as the rack hook is lifted, the rack should fall immediately on the snail, and the warning pin in the striking train fall on the warning piece. Space will not permit of dealing with the number of faults to be found in the striking work. The most common are: clock strikes on the warning; this will not give the rack sufficient time to fall on the snail; obviously the wrong number struck. Rack spring too weak gives the same result. In the former the warning piece or the pin can easily be bent. The rack spring will usually bend to give more power. When the power is gone a new one is advisable. A loose rack tail is tightened with a few taps from the pene of a hammer. Refrain from filing a piece unless certain the alteration will cure a fault. Should the clock strike one at five minutes to the hour, and one short at the hour, the wheel that carries the pins for lifting the hammer must be shifted a tooth or so forward in the pinion with which it gears. It will be found that in its faulty condition, when the clock finishes striking at the hour, it raises the hammer to such a position that it drops off when the clock warns five minutes before the hour, thus giving the one blow mentioned. It then gathers up one tooth of the striking rack, leaving it one blow short at the hour when the clock strikes. Should the clock, immediately after striking, make a clattering noise, it will probably be due to the hammer chattering on the stop pin or spring, and the noise can be lessened by slipping a rubber tube on the pin. Bicycle valve tube is sometimes handy for this purpose in clocks.

The striking work having been examined, it may be removed and the plates taken apart for general cleaning and overhauling. On reassembling, place the going and striking trains in the frame and pin the top plate on. Put the lifting piece on its stud, the rack, the rack hook, the gathering pallet and minute wheel, and try the warning. The warning pin, which is in the wheel between the plates, should have half a turn before it falls on the detent. To correct this, lift the top plate, move the wheel round a tooth, and replace it in the hole.

English Regulators.—An English "Regulator" is a time-piece of high precision. In some respects, its construction resembles an enlarged version of a Vienna Regulator, but in others it is similar to the timekeeping part of a long-case, or "grandfather" clock. A fine example is shown in Figs. 65, 66, and 67, and it will be seen that the dial is of special form, the object being to assist in very accurate reading.

English Regulators almost invariably have dead-beat escapements and compensated "seconds" pendulums. The pendulum is usually hung on a special bracket which is bolted to the back board of the case. In some instances, this bracket is part of a massive casting which also supports the movement, and takes the place of the usual seat-board of a long-case clock.

Some form of maintaining-power, usually of the "going ratchet" type, as used in the Vienna clocks, is always fitted. The motion-work is modified to suit the special dial, and the hour hand arbor may be driven from the centre wheel, as shown in the illustrations, or by an extra wheel fitted on the back of the main wheel of the train.

The cleaning of these clocks should not present any difficulty to the careful craftsman, but the greatest care must be taken to ensure that everything is in perfect order if precise timekeeping is to be obtained.

CHAPTER 15

Synchronous Electric Clocks

"SYNCHRONOUS" clocks are the most recently introduced form of domestic timekeepers, and, provided that suitable supplies of frequency-controlled alternating current are available, are quite satisfactory for general use.

Strictly, synchronous clocks are not really clocks at all, for they do not, in themselves, possess any timekeeping mechanism, but are merely "repeaters", controlled by the frequency, or number of cycles per second, of the alternating current flowing in the supply mains to which they are connected. This frequency is, in turn, governed by the power station, and is, so far as possible, kept at a definite pre-determined standard. If, for any reason, the frequency of the current departs from the set standard, all the clocks connected to the circuit concerned will vary from true time by an amount depending on the variation of frequency of the alternating current.

The principle of operation of synchronous clocks is that they are driven by a small electric motor of what is called the "synchronous" type. This motor is so constructed that its speed of rotation is governed by the number of cycles of alternation of the current supply to which the motor is connected. The motor, in fact, turns in exact step, or "in synchronism" with the alternations of the current. If the frequency increases, and there are more cycles per second, the motor will run faster, and conversely, if the frequency decreases, and there are fewer cycles per second, the motor will run slower.

In synchronous clocks, the motor is linked to the clock hands by a train of reduction gearing which provides the necessary step-down ratio to rotate the hands at the correct speed to indicate time so long as the alternating current is maintained at the correct frequency. In Great Britain, the standard frequency is 50 cycles per second, but in some other countries other standards are in operation. The clocks must, therefore, be constructed to run in step with the particular frequency of supply to which they are to be connected.

The motors used for synchronous clocks usually consist of a simple iron frame, called a "stator", which is magnetically energized by a coil, known as an "energizing coil", mounted on the iron frame at a suitable point. The stator is arranged to embrace the rotating part of the motor, which is known as the "rotor", and both stator and rotor are provided with pole-pieces which pass close to one another as the rotor revolves. Normally, these small synchronous motors are not self-starting, but, once an initial turn has been given to their rotors, they will continue to rotate at a speed that is perfectly in step with the cycles of the alternating current until some interruption causes them to stop. After this, they will again require to be started. Some motors are fitted with a starting device to overcome the need for hand starting, but the basic principle of operation remains unaltered.

The rotation of the rotor is caused by the changing magnetic polarity of the stator, which is, in turn, set up by the reversals of the current flowing in the energizing coil. This, together with the familiar law of magnetism that "like poles repel, and unlike poles attract", and the momentum of the rotor, causes the latter to move round a distance equal to the space between each pole on the stator and the next at each reversal of the current. For this reason, the motor is called "synchronous".

In order to enable the motor to run at a speed sufficiently low to drive the clock through simple gearing, the pole-pieces of the stator are usually sub-divided into a number of small "poles", and the corresponding poles on the rotor step forward from one stator pole to the next at each alternation. The speed usually chosen for the motor is 200 r.p.m. which is a very convenient one for the gear train.

There are two types of rotor, one form being of soft iron, and the other of steel, permanently magnetized. In the former type, the magnetization of the iron is caused by induction from the magnetic field of the stator, but in the latter, the stator only has to produce its own magnetic field, which acts on the existing field of the rotor. Both types are good, though the permanently magnetized form is usually more powerful.

There are also two types of reduction gearing in general use, one being of the normal wheel-and-pinion form, and the other an assembly of worm-reduction gearing. Both types are good, and some makers have adopted a combination of both worm and wheel-and-pinion gearing for the trains of some models.

The repair of synchronous clocks should not present any difficulty to the horologist of average skill, for the construction of most models is simple and straightforward. At the same time it must be remembered that these clocks are connected to the public supply mains when in operation, and that every care must be taken to see that everything, particularly in matters connected with insulation, is in perfect order. Neglect at such points may spell serious danger to the user. The electrical connections are usually of the simplest for there is only one simple coil, or at the most two, and even when the arrangements are a little more complex, as in the case of synchronous alarm clocks, only common sense and care are needed.

One of the best known makes of synchronous clocks is the "Sectric", manufactured by Smith's English Clocks, Ltd., of Cricklewood, London. There have been several models of "Sectric" clocks, but most of them follow the same general lines. The earliest model employed wheel-and-pinion type reducing gearing, and was driven by a motor fitted with a permanently magnetized rotor. The

I

stator was formed of two ring-shaped iron pressings which, when fitted together, enclosed the stator coil. This proved to be a very compact and reliable arrangement, and is still retained for some of their later models. The stator of the early type was mounted in a moulded plastic housing which also formed the enclosing drum for the rest of the clock movement. A small pillar-and-plate frame contained the wheels and pinions, and was secured to the moulding by three screws. The rotor, which was of the permanently-magnetized form, ran in oil-cup bearings, one of which was located in the moulded drum, and the other on the front plate of the train frame. The cleaning and oiling of a clock of this type is an easy job, and does not call for more than a few comments. Care should be taken to clean thoroughly and refill both the oil-cup bearings of the rotor spindle, and when the train frame is being re-fitted to the moulded drum, the front rotor pivot should be carefully guided into its bearing, for undue force may lead to damage. The floating endplate which is held by a flat spring in the assembly of this front rotor bearing should be smooth on its acting face, and highly polished. If pitted, it should be replaced, and the rotor pivot may also need smoothing and polishing.

It is not wise to attempt to remove the stator of this model from its moulded housing, for its leads are soldered direct to the two contact pins on the rear of the drum, and any loosening of the coil will almost certainly sever these leads. In any case, failure of the stator coil is very rare, and if it does occur, its correction should be carried out by the makers. Clock oil is the right lubricant for the pivots of the train, and very light grease, which may even be thinned a trifle with clock-oil, should be used for the oil-cup bearings and for the fabric-plastic wheel that engages with the rotor pinion. Before taking the train frame out of the drum, note the action of the motor-starting arm, and the way that it is rocked by the cone-cam on the setting spindle and be sure that the action is

Fig. 68.—Movement of Small Synchronous Timepiece.
(Type Name, "Bijou".) Made by Smith's English Clocks Ltd.

A—Frame Plate; B—Stator Frame (enclosing Stator Coil); C—Termina
Block; D—Setting and Starting Assembly ("Bottom Set" type); J—
Moulded Enclosing Case; K—Case Retaining Screw; L—Slot for Setting
Spindle.

correct when the clock is reassembled. Another point that
should be noted is that the knurled knob on the setting
spindle is screwed on with a *left-hand* thread, and is locked
by a small set-screw.

The following "Sectric" clock model had a similar
motor and starting arrangement, but the stator was
attached to the train-frame plate, and the reduction gearing
consisted of two stages of worm gearing and one stage of
wheel-and-pinion gearing. Known as the "De-Luxe", this
model is very reliable. Two of its spindles had oil-cup
bearings, but the assembly was simple, and these clocks
can be handled quite easily when they call for cleaning and
repair.

**Fig. 69.—Front Plate View of Small Syn-
chronous Timepiece. (Type Name, "Bijou".)
Made by Smith's English Clocks Ltd.**

A—Frame Plate; D—Setting and Starting Assembly
("Bottom Set" Type); E—Minute Wheel and Pinion
of Motion Work; F—Minute, Hour, and Seconds
Hand Spindle and Pipes; G—Seconds Hand Drive
Wheel (not always fitted); H—Bridge for Attach-
ment to Case.

Still another "Sectric" timepiece is the "Bijou", which
has a motor resembling that of the other two models, but
of smaller size. The train is of the wheel-and-pinion type,
and all the wheel spindles are made in the form of pipes,
which run on steel pins spanning the two frame-plates.
Again, the assembly is a simple one, which can be dealt
with quite well by any horologist. Be careful to clean the
holes in the pipes of all the wheels, and apply oil to the
steel pins on which they pivot *before* putting them in
position. There have been two types of rotor bearings
fitted to this model, one in which the bearing pin was

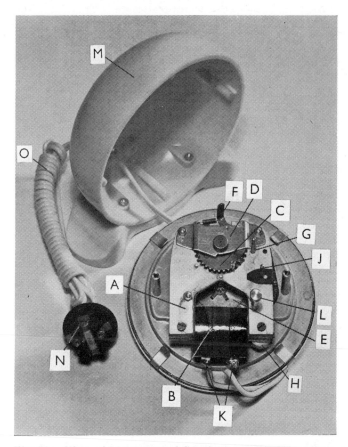

Fig. 70.—View of Movement of Synchronous Electric Alarm Clock. (Type Name, "New Callboy".) Made by Smith's English Clocks Ltd.

A—Stator Frame; B—Stator Energizing Coil; C—Rotor; D—Rotor Bearing Plate; E—Centre Wheel of Time Train; F—Starter Lever and Spring; G—Set-Hands Spindle; H—Alarm Buzzer Armature; J—Alarm Setting Spindle; K—Terminals of Energizing Coil; L—Alarm Silencing Push Rod; M—Moulded Plastic Case; N—Connector Plug, with Fuse; O—Plastic-covered Connecting Lead.

fixed to a bush in the centre of the stator frame, and the other in which the pin is fixed to the rotor itself. In either case, the lubrication is the same, oil being supplied to the hole in the sleeve and thus spread along the bearing as the rotor is replaced. The later types have sintered bearings, but this does not alter the method of applying oil. Lubricate the set-and-start spindle, and the friction points of the starter-arm, and make sure that the small flat spring on this arm does spin the rotor when the starting operation is carried out.

There have also been several models of "Sectric" alarm clocks, but these are adaptations of the timepiece models, with the addition of an alarm buzzer and its separate energizing coil, and the necessary contacts. In some of the later alarm clocks, the alarm buzzer coil is always energized, and the release device merely brings the vibrating reed into its field to sound the alarm, and rocks it away when the silencing control is operated. Careful examination will soon reveal the action in all these models.

The Ferranti is another well-known make of synchronous clock. In this type, the rotor is of the non-magnetized form, and the energizing coil is fitted to a flat stator made up of several thin iron plates, or laminations. Early models used wheel-and-pinion type reduction gearing, but the latest form employs worm gearing. Starting is carried out by spinning a small knob fitted to the extended pivot of one of the train spindles. This rotates the fabric-plastic wheel which engages with the rotor pinion, and so starts the motor.

A small, but heavy, resiliently mounted flywheel is fitted to the rotor spindle to maintain the rotation during momentary interruptions of current, and care should be taken to see that this flywheel has a certain amount of free movement under the control of its spring. This spring resembles a simple balance-spring, and it forms the link between the flywheel and the rotor spindle.

The alarm version of the Ferranti synchronous clock has

Fig. 71.—Ferranti Synchronous Alarm Clock.

A—Frame Plate; B—Stator; C—Rotor; D—Rotor Flywheel; E—Oil-cup
Bearing for Rotor; F—Stator Coil; G—First Wheel and Worm of Train;
H—Second Wheel and Worm of Train; J—Starting Knob; K—Setting
Knob; L—Alarm Setting Spindle; N—Dial Plate; O—Leads to Coil.

a 24-hour alarm release mechanism, which is arranged to
permit the alarm to sound only once in 24 hours. When this
mechanism is being reassembled, care must be taken to
ensure that the "A.M." and "P.M." readings which appear
through a small hole in the dial agree with those on the
setting dial on the back of the clock. In other words, if
the alarm is set for 6 a.m. then, when the hands are turned

until the alarm sounds at the correct time, the "A" for a.m. must be showing through the hole in the main dial of the clock. If this is not so, then the small nut in the centre of the setting dial must be removed, and the dial taken off and turned through 180 degrees, after which it must again be secured by the nut. Make sure, also, that the change of letter from "A" to "P", and vice versa takes place at 12 midnight and 12 midday, and if it does not, readjust the position of the clock hands accordingly.

The Metamec is another good form of synchronous clock, and in its general form, it resembles the Ferranti, the rotor being of the non-magnetized type, and the train consisting of worm gearing. A novel feature of this make is that it has a small ratchet click built into the movement which makes a steady, but subdued "ticking" sound when the clock is running. This tick can be silenced if the user does not want it, but it is a useful indication that the clock is running in models not provided with a seconds hand on the dial. The starting of the Metamec clock is by the rotation of a small knob that lifts and releases a small "flick" arm, and when reassembling one of these clocks, make sure that this flick action is acting correctly, and giving the rotor a smart spin.

The Goblin synchronous clock employs a motor which is very similar to that of the Sectric clock, and its train is of the wheel-and-pinion form. As the motor is self-starting, a direction control is fitted to ensure that the motor always runs in the right direction. This takes the form of a fabric-plastic cam on the spindle next to that of the rotor, and a small rocking lever, also of fabric-plastic, which rocks on a pivot at one end, and encloses the cam in a stepped hole in the other. The engagement of the steps in the hole in the lever with the projections on the cam disc allows the spindle to revolve in one direction, but locks it against rotation in the opposite one. By this means, the rotor is compelled to turn in the right direction. This device is typical of those fitted to all self-starting synchronous

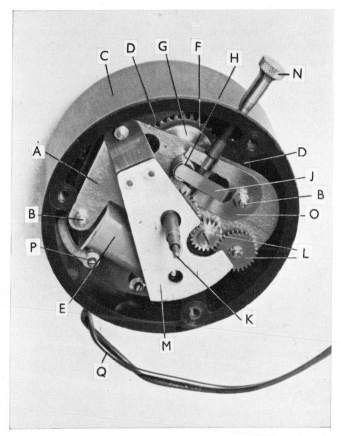

Fig. 72.—Front View of Metamec Synchronous Electric Alarm Clock Movement.

A—Frame Plate; B—Frame Attachment Nuts; C—Moulded Plastic Case, which also forms part of the Clock Frame; D—Stator; E—Stator Energizing Coil; F—Rotor; G—Rotor Flywheel; H—Oil-cup Rotor Bearing (Spring-loaded type); J—Rotor Bearing Loading Spring; K—Concentric Hour, Minute and Seconds Spindles and Pipes; L—Alarm-setting Gear Train; M—Alarm Buzzer Armature; N—Alarm Releasing and Silencing Knob; O—Clamp-spring for Alarm Releasing and Setting Knob; P—Connections to Coil Winding; Q—Flex Leads for External connection to Supply.

clocks, but in some cases the directional control is fitted on the rotor spindle itself.

The Temco synchronous clock differs in detail from those already described, for its motor is so constructed that the poles of the permanently-magnetized rotor enclose, or rather sweep over, those of the stator. The stator coil is enclosed in an iron cup, the top of the wall of which is slotted to form one set of poles, while a disc, set on the end of an iron core mounted in the centre of the cup, has corresponding slots round its circumference to form the opposite poles. The core is bored centrally, and two bronze bearings are fitted to carry the pin on which the rotor is fixed. The rotor is in the form of a straight bar, the ends of which are bent over and slotted to form poles. It is fixed on one end of the bearing pin, and the latter, after passing through the bearings in the stator core, carries the drive pinion at its opposite end. The rest of the clock mechanism is simple, and its assembly is self-evident. When refixing the motor, do not omit to replace the small casing and lid which enclose it.

The synchronous clocks described are typical of most of the makes on the market. All makes will fall into one or other of the general forms dealt with, and a little care and patience will soon enable the repairer to deal with the special points of construction of various models. The main cause of failure of synchronous clocks is nearly always lack of lubrication, and cleaning and oiling will almost always effect a cure. Where wear has taken place, a spare part of the correct kind is nearly always to be had. Other troubles met with are few, but perhaps the most annoying is persistent humming. This is always caused by some loose part, usually of iron, which is vibrating in step with the alternating current. The cure is to fasten the part concerned more firmly. For instance, loose stator components may hum quite loudly, and the screwing down of fixing screws usually stops this effectually. Similar methods apply to other parts. A coil may vibrate if loose on its core on the stator. The remedy is obvious.

Fig. 73.—Front View of Synchronous Chiming Clock. Made by Smith's English Clocks Ltd.

A—Frame Plates; C—Centre Wheel of Time Train; D—Warning Detent; E—Rack Hook; F—Gathering Pallet; G—Rack; H—Let-Off Detent; J—Chiming Train Locking-Plate; L—Underslung Sub-Frame for Chime Barrel and Hammers; M—Chiming and Striking Hammers; O—Chiming and Striking Silencing Lever; P—Motion Work Wheels and Striking Snail; R—Lower Case Attachment Lug; S—Upper Case Attachment Lugs.

A broken down coil winding is one item that is beyond the usual repairer. The wire is so fine in gauge that it is best to return the coil to the makers, and to obtain a new one. If this is impossible, then re-winding should be entrusted to experts. Unskilled work here is dangerous.

Finally, take special care with connections on flex leads

Fig. 74.—Back view of Synchronous Chiming Clock. Made by Smith's English Clocks Ltd.

A—Frame Plates; B—Synchronous Motor in Housing; K—Chime Barrel Drive Wheel; L—Underslung Sub-Frame for Chime Barrel and Hammers; M—Group of Chiming and Striking Hammers; N—Lifting Lever for Striking Hammers; P—Motion Work Wheel; R—Lower Case Attachment Lug; S—Upper Case Attachment Lug (one of two).

and do not tolerate poor quality flex, or flex that is in bad condition. See that plugs and terminal screws are properly fitted, and only bare the minimum amount of wire when making connections. Remember that you are dealing with the supply mains, and that the standard of wiring must be as high as that necessary for other domestic electrical appliances.

CHAPTER 16

Electric Master-Clocks and Impulse Dials

THE system of electrical timekeeping in which a high-precision master-clock operates a circuit of impulse dials at half-minute intervals is one of the best, most reliable, and most accurate of modern horological mechanisms, and is steadily becoming more and more popular as its qualities become better known.

As well as being widely adopted for driving large numbers of dials in big buildings, master-clocks of the impulse type are being increasingly installed as "regulators" by horologists, both professional and amateur, on account of their fine timekeeping and easy maintenance. These advantages arise from their simple construction and correct theoretical design and the fact that they draw their power from a battery of dry-cells or accumulators, which renders them completely independent of failures of the supply mains.

There are a number of makes of master-clocks and impulse dials, but most of them are very similar in general principles. The Synchronome, based on the designs of the late F. Hope-Jones, F.R.A.S., a pioneer in electric clock construction, is manufactured by the Synchronome Company, Ltd., and is shown in Figs. 76 and 77.

As these illustrations show, the mechanism of both master-clock and dial is very simple. In the master-clock (Fig. 77), a pendulum P, beating seconds, carries on its rod a gathering click B which steps over one tooth of the 15-toothed ratchet-wheel C every time the pendulum swings to the left. As the pendulum returns to the right, it then moves the wheel forward one tooth. This, of course, means that the wheel makes one complete rotation every 30 seconds.

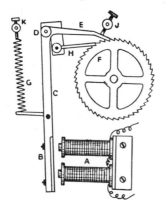

Fig. 75.—Early Form of
Impulse Dial. Mechanism
now superseded.

A—Electro-magnet.
B—Armature.
C—Armature Lever.
D—Pivot of Driving Paw
E—Driving Pawl.
F—120-toothed Ratchet Wheel.
G—Return Spring.
H—Backstop Pawl.
J—Limit Stop.
K—Tension Screw.

On the same spindle as the ratchet-wheel is a vane D, and as the wheel completes a rotation, this vane engages with and trips a small spring-loaded catch K drawing it aside and then releasing it. Resting on this catch is the end of a right-angled gravity-arm G and when the catch is tripped, this arm falls by its own weight. As it does so, a roller R mounted on the arm rolls down the specially formed inclined face on the impulse bracket J which is mounted on the pendulum rod. By this means, the weight of the arm, which is pivoted on the spindle F, is able to

Fig. 76. — Mechanism of
Impulse-driven Dial of the
Synchronome System.

A—120-toothed main wheel.
B—Electro-magnet.
C—Armature.
D—Armature Lever.
E—Driving Click or Pawl.
F—Driving Spring, or Return
Spring.
G—Backstop Lever.
H—Momentum Stop.
I — Stroke Limit Stop.

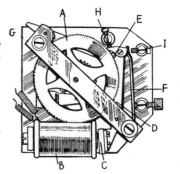

give the pendulum an impulse which is sufficient to maintain its swing.

As the gravity-arm reaches the bottom of its travel, the part of it which is at right angles to the main portion makes contact with a screw set in the tip of the armature A and thereby completes the electrical circuit through the winding of the magnet M. This magnet then attracts the armature A and so raises the gravity-arm and replaces it on the catch K where it remains until it is again released at the end of a further 30 seconds. As the arm is replaced on the catch, the contacts on the arm and the armature separate, and the circuit is broken. As soon as this happens the armature falls back to its original position.

From this it will be seen that the pendulum merely has

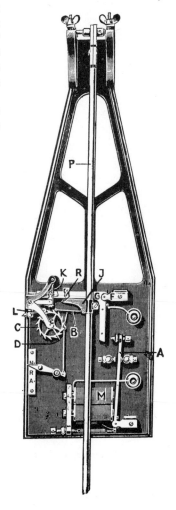

Fig. 77. — Diagram of the Master-clock Mechanism of a Synchronome System Clock.

P—Pendulum.
J—Impulse Bracket.
B—Gathering Pallet.
C—15-toothed Wheel.
D—Vane.
F—Pivot Point of Gravity-Arm.
G—Gravity-arm.
K—Gravity-arm Catch.
L—Backstop Arm.
M—Electro-magnet.
A—Armature.
R—Roller (on Gravity-arm).

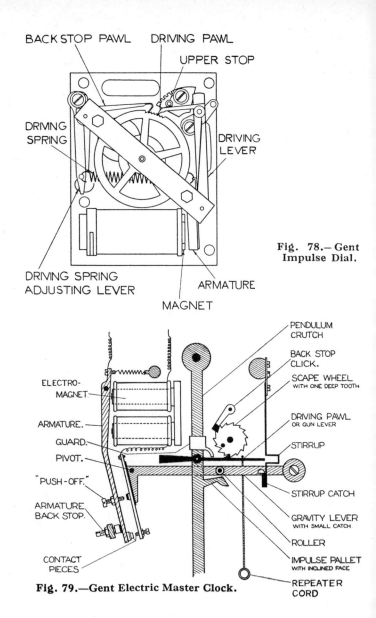

BACK STOP PAWL   DRIVING PAWL

UPPER STOP

DRIVING SPRING

DRIVING LEVER

DRIVING SPRING ADJUSTING LEVER

ARMATURE

MAGNET

Fig. 78.— Gent Impulse Dial.

PENDULUM CRUTCH

BACK STOP CLICK.

SCAPE WHEEL WITH ONE DEEP TOOTH

ELECTRO-MAGNET

ARMATURE.

GUARD.

PIVOT.

"PUSH-OFF."

ARMATURE BACK STOP.

CONTACT PIECES

DRIVING PAWL OR GUN LEVER

STIRRUP

STIRRUP CATCH

GRAVITY LEVER WITH SMALL CATCH

ROLLER

IMPULSE PALLET WITH INCLINED FACE

REPEATER CORD

Fig. 79.—Gent Electric Master Clock.

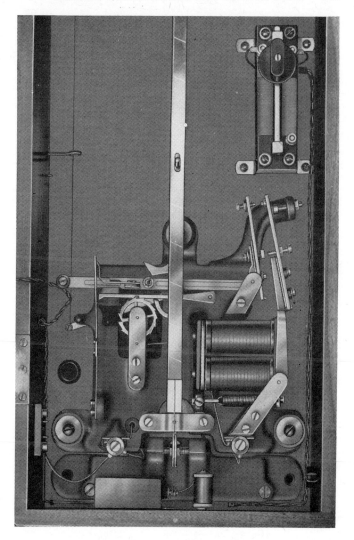

Fig. 80.—Gent Master Clock

K

to propel one light ratchet wheel tooth-by-tooth, and is, therefore, particularly free from any interference with its swing. This is the reason for its excellent timekeeping.

The impulse-dial mechanisms operated by the master-clock are also very simple, as can be seen by Fig. 83. They consist of a 120-toothed wheel mounted on the spindle carrying the minute hand. Engaging with the wheel is a driving pawl, or click U, which pivots on a screw set in the end of the armature O which can be attracted by the electro magnet Y.

The magnet windings of all the dials and the magnet winding of the master-clock are all in series with the battery, and so, when the gravity arm on the master-clock

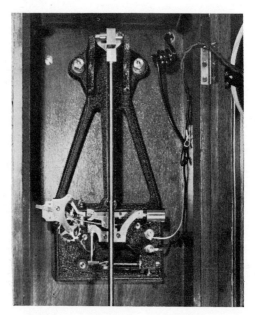

Fig. 81.—Mechanism of a Gillett & Johnston Master Clock.

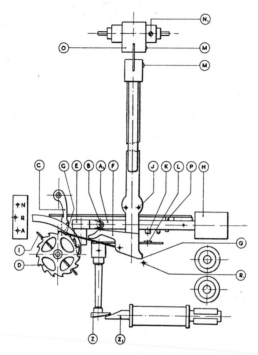

Fig. 82.—Diagram of Mechanisms of Gillett & Johnston Electric Master Clock and Impulse Dial.

A_1—Gravity Lever, or Arm; B—Impulsing Roller; C—Trip Catch for Gravity Lever; D—15-toothed Ratchet Wheel; E—Rebound Damper; F—Impulse Pallet; G—Jewelled Gathering Pallet; H—Adjustable Counterweight for Gravity Lever; I—Trip Release Vane on Ratchet Wheel Spindle; J—Crutch Pins; K—Electrical Contact Point on Gravity Lever; L—Electrical Contact Point on Armature Lever; M—Screws Fixing Pendulum Suspension Spring; N—Suspension Trunnion Fixing Screw; O—Suspension Trunnion; P—Gravity Lever Latch Spring; Q—Crutch; R_1—Armature Lever Limit-Stop Pin; Z—Armature Lever and Armature; Z_1—Electro-magnet Pole.

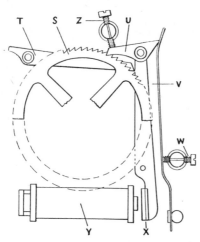

Fig. 83.— Diagram of Impulse Dial Mechanism made by Gillett & Johnston Ltd., of Croydon.

S—120-toothed Ratchet Wheel; T—Back-stop Lever; U—Driving Pawl or Click; V—Return Spring; W—Réturn Spring Tension Adjustment Screw; X—Armature Lever; Y—Electro-magnet; Z—Driving Pawl Limit Stop Screw.

closes the circuit by touching the contact-screw on the armature, all the dial magnets are energized by current from the battery. This causes their armature levers to be rocked, and their driving clicks to step into the next tooth on their 120-toothed wheels. As the levers rock, they also store energy in the small flat return springs, shown at v in the illustration. As soon as the circuit is broken by the replacement of the gravity arm of the master-clock, the magnets of the dials release their armatures, and the return springs push the levers back to their original positions, advancing the minute hands one half-minute as they do so.

The completion of the contact in the master-clock is, therefore, all that is necessary to advance all the dials in the circuit one half-minute. In the illustration of the dial mechanism, the lever T seen behind the 120-toothed wheel S is the backstop, which prevents the wheel from moving backwards, and the screws Z and W are limit stops for the driving click and the armature lever respectively.

Almost any number of dials can be driven from the master-clock, provided that the battery power is also increased in proportion, and in addition, the half-minute impulses can be used to control time-recorders, time-switches, bell-signals, and large tower clocks up to any size.

Another form of master-clock and impulse dial installation is that manufactured by Messrs. Gent & Co., of Leicester. The master-clock mechanism is shown diagrammatically in Fig. 79. Here the pendulum (not shown) carries with it a pendulum crutch, on which is mounted the driving pawl. This steps over the teeth of the 15-toothed ratchet wheel, and propels them, tooth-by-tooth. The wheel has one tooth that is cut deeper than the rest, and this is used to actuate the release mechanism. At each swing to the right, the tip of the driving pawl enters a slot formed in the stirrup, and so does not engage with the stirrup itself, but when the pawl falls into the deeper tooth, the tip of the pawl does engage with the stirrup, and thrusts it aside. This releases the gravity lever, which, as it descends, delivers an impulse to the pendulum crutch through the roller

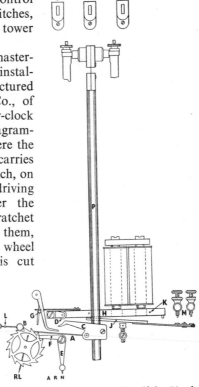

Fig. 84.—Diagram of English Clock Systems, Ltd. Master Clock.

A—Gathering Click; B—Back Stop Roller; C—Pallet; D—Roller; E and F—Controlled Lever; G—Catch; H—Gravity Arm or Lever; J—Rebound Spring; K—Pivot Front of Gravity Lever; L—Backstop; M—Contacts; P—Pendulum; RL—15-toothed Wheel with Release Lever.

which is mounted on the lever. The roller runs down the impulse pallet on the crutch as the latter swings to the left. Then, as with the Synchronome clock, the gravity lever closes contacts at the end of its descent, and so energizes the electro-magnet. This, through its armature, replaces the gravity lever on the catch on the stirrup, the dials all being advanced at the same time.

Still another form of master-clock mechanism is shown in Fig. 82, this being that manufactured by Messrs. Gillett & Johnston, Ltd., of Croydon. It is very similar to the Synchronome master-clock, except that the armature is chamfered, and swings towards a pair of similarly chamfered poles on the electro-magnet. The object of this arrangement is to obtain very silent action. Another feature is that the gravity arm has an adjustable counterpoise weight, which enables the impulse to be adjusted to suit the pendulum. The dial mechanism in this system is practically identical with that of the Synchronome type.

Yet another model is that made by English Clock Systems, Ltd., a subsidiary of Messrs. Smith's English Clocks, Ltd. Again, the master-clock mechanism is made on the same lines, but the electro-magnet acts directly on the gravity arm, which carries the armature of the magnet as a part of it. The dial mechanisms are similar to those already described. (Fig. 84.)

About the only attention required by these clocks is the maintenance of the battery, and the very occasional application of a small drop of watch or chronometer oil to the frictional parts, such as the pivots of the 15-toothed wheel, the pivots of the gravity-arm and the roller mounted on it, and so on. Very occasionally, the pivots and friction points of the dial mechanisms will also need a small amount of oil.

For small installations, consisting of the master-clock and one or two dials, large size dry-cells of good quality form the best battery. For larger circuits, accumulator batteries arranged for trickle-charging are ideal.

CHAPTER 17

Adding Quarter-Chimes to Grandfather Clocks

MANY people who possess grandfather striking clocks wish to add chimes to them. Given a clock the wheels and pinions of which are sound and not badly worn, and which has a good case, there is no reason why this should not be done; and there are many amateurs capable of carrying out the necessary alterations when aided by proper directions.

To undertake the job with any chance of success, a good small lathe, or a large pair of clock turns or clockmaker's "throw", a bench, a vice, and numerous small files, drills, broaches, etc., will be wanted; and, above all, the ability to work fairly well in metal. As none but fairly good mechanics will attempt such work, it is not necessary that elementary details relating to the working of the clock or the execution of small mechanical operations of the ordinary kind should be minutely described.

Making New Frame.—Fig. 85 shows a general view of a grandfather striking-clock movement. To convert it to a chime clock, it will be necessary to add a third barrel and train of wheels on the right-hand side, very similar to the striking train of wheels on the left. It is obvious at a glance that there is no room in the frame for this addition; therefore the best and only really practical way is to discard the old plates and make a new frame. This doubtless appears to be a formidable undertaking, but is not so in reality. In some cases the old pillars can be saved and used again, especially if they are large in diameter and strong; but generally it will be found advisable to turn four new ones. As movements differ somewhat in size and general proportions, exact dimensions of any part cannot

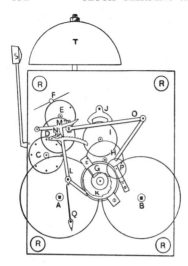

Fig. 85. — Movement of Grandfather Striking Clock.

be given; each worker must, according to his own case, work them out for himself. The new plates should, as a rule, be a trifle higher than the old ones—say $\frac{1}{2}$ in. to 1 in. —and 3 in. wider, which usually makes the movement about $8\frac{1}{2}$ in. square. For the plates, procure two pieces of the required dimensions and from $\frac{1}{8}$ in. to $\frac{3}{16}$ in. thick, the latter thickness being better. All the metal, etc., may be procured from material dealers, and there are certain firms who will, for a trifling sum, also planish the brass for the plates—that is, hammer it flat and true, and polish the surfaces until they are almost like glass; this will save an immense amount of labour, and produce a finish that no amateur could hope to attain.

Castings should not be used for the pillars; the metal will be too soft. They should be cut from a length of $\frac{5}{8}$-in. round brass rod, and turned. In making a clock frame, the object to be kept steadily in view is to produce a firm, rigid frame, true and squarely built up. Fancy pillars, polished plates, etc., are not necessary, and in many cases may tend to weaken the parts; so that, unless time is no object, the pillars can be used as they leave the lathe, and the plates will not require any more polishing than the file or emery buff has given them. The letter references in Fig. 85 are as follows: A the striking barrel, B the going barrel, C the pin wheel, D the pallet wheel, E the warning wheel, F the fly, G the centre wheel, H the third wheel, I the 'scape wheel, J the pallets, K the snail, L the rack, M the rack hook or detent, N the gathering pallet, O the warning or discharging lever, P the minute wheel, Q the rack spring, R the pillars, S the hammer, and T the bell.

In Fig. 86 is shown the new frame on a smaller scale. First take the two plates, and draw a centre line down each. Clamp the plates together, and on the centre line, close to each end, drill them both right through with a drill about $\frac{1}{16}$ in. wide. Rivet them together lightly with brass rivets, and file up square and true on the edges. Mark and drill the pillar holes, $\frac{5}{16}$ in. in diameter, right through both. Note that the top right-hand hole is placed 1 in. in from the side. This is to clear the hammer rack for the chime bells. The plates can then be separated by knocking out the rivets. These rivet holes will be found useful when drilling pivot-holes, etc., for after drilling the holes in one plate the plates can be lightly pinned together,

Fig. 86.—Frame of Grandfather Clock.

and the back plate drilled through the front one. The rivet-holes can be left, as they will do no harm. The pillars can be screwed into the back plate up to a shoulder, or a screw can be driven into them through the plate, or they can be riveted like the old ones. Perhaps this latter is the better and easier way. The pillars should come through the front plate and be pinned, as in the old frame.

"Pitching" the Going and Striking Trains.—The frame having been made, the going and striking trains can be "pitched in". Fig. 87 shows the position of wheels, etc., and the letter references are as follows: A the hour snail, B the hour rack, C the hour-rack hook, D the hour warning lever, E the quarter snail, F the quarter rack, G the quarter-rack hook, H the quarter lifting and warning lever, I the pin in the quarter rack, J the lifting-pin in the warning lever, K the chime-hammer rack, L the chime-hammer

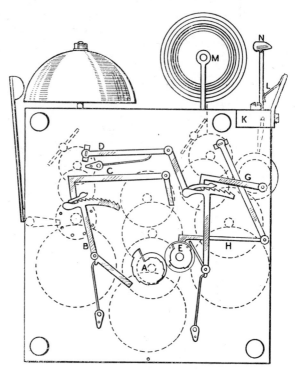

Fig. 87.—Going, Chiming, and Striking Trains
of Grandfather Clock, after reconstruction.

springs, M the chime bells, N the chime hammer, and O the
chime barrel or drum and pins.

The going train must be pivoted all on the centre line.
The positions of the pivot-holes can be obtained by measurement from the old plates, or they may be transferred direct
by marking through the old holes. After drilling, the plates
may be pinned together and the holes drilled in the back
plates. The holes should be carefully opened out by
broaches, so that they fit the pivots easily, but without

shake. Always oil broaches when using them. If the depths are not quite right when run in, the imperfect holes must be opened out by broaching them larger, plugged with brass, and re-drilled.

In pitching the striking train, note that the palle:-wheel holes must be at exactly the same distance from the centre-wheel holes of the going train as in the old movement, or the striking rack will not be correct. This distance must be most carefully made exactly the same as before, and may necessitate the pin-wheel being placed in a different position from that shown in either Fig. 85 or Fig. 87. The position of the pallet-wheel pivot-hole must be first determined, and the pin-wheel then planted in such a position as to run properly with both main-wheel and pallet-wheel pinion. The back plate will require cutting to admit of the pallets being taken out, and the back-cock or pendulum suspension cock must be screwed on in its proper place. In pitching the going train, the barrel must be placed as low as possible without fouling the wooden seat-board. The hour hammer and its check spring, etc., can be re-planted in the new frame as in the old one. Possibly, the hammer may want a longer stem, on account of the increased height of the frame.

Motion Work.—The motion work can be made as before, the cannon pinion put on, the "bridge" screwed and steady-pinned on, and the hour-wheel mounted. If the old snail was on the hour-wheel, the rack stud can be screwed in again, its position being carefully located by compasses, making it bear exactly the same relationship to the hour-wheel and pallet-wheel as before. Its spring can be planted and the rack put on. Try the rack all round the hours very carefully, and, if necessary, alter the tail and pin, and make a new one to suit the new pitching. Here the worker's skill is required in order to determine the amount and direction of the alterations necessary to restore the rack action to its previous accuracy. The warning lever, which engages the pin in the warning wheel, can be planted as shown in Fig. 87, a new tail made to it, and the necessary slot cut in the front plate. But the old rack hook will be discarded for one of a different shape. Its stud, however, can be used again in a new position.

Minute-wheel.—The minute-wheel may be planted in the same position as before. If it has a steel pinion and is held by a cock and screw, plant in the cock in an upright position, with the screw downwards. If it has a brass pinion and works on a stud, it will be better to turn a new pinion and mount in a cock screwed to the plate. If the hour rack works on a separate star-wheel with jumper and spring, plant all exactly as before, taking care to run nothing too close to the winding square of the striking barrel, and to leave room for the key to be placed on it.

Chiming Train.—The train of wheels for the chiming side should now be taken in hand. When purchasing, ask for a rough barrel of ordinary size for the chime side of a grandfather quarter clock, a main wheel of 100 teeth, second wheel of 80, pallet wheel of 63, warning wheel of 56, and chime wheel of 40. Pinions can be purchased ready almost for riveting on the wheels, and pivot or pinion wire may be bought in lengths, and will require turning down, hardening, tempering, etc. If the latter plan is adopted (and it is the best), order with the wheels half a length of pinion wire of eight leaves to suit the main wheel, half a length of eight leaves to suit the 80 wheel, and a length of seven leaves to suit the 63 and 56 wheels. The pinions on which the 80 and 63 wheels are mounted have eight leaves; the pinions of the 56 wheel and the "fly" pinion have seven leaves. Procure also a piece of $1\frac{1}{4}$-in. brass tube, 2 in. long, for the chime barrel in which the pins are to be fixed.

Large Barrel.—The large barrel will be found to be mounted on a rough arbor, turned roughly, with the spiral groove for the line cut, and the ratchet cast on and cut. Place this in the lathe, and smooth up the ends and all surfaces; turn the arbor down true, and also the pivots and groove for the "key" which fastens the wheel. The

striking or going barrel can be
taken as a pattern, so no illustration is necessary.

Fig. 88 shows the relative positions of barrel, wheels and pinions,
and "fly", A being the pipe of fly,
B the curved or bow-spring, and C
the pin to hold the pipe and spring.

The barrel pivots must be
turned as smooth as possible, and
finished with a very smooth file.
After this they are polished by
means of a brass, bell-metal, or
steel polisher, which is filed
smooth, and has oil-stone dust
and oil spread on it. Use the
polisher as a file with light pressure
while the arbor runs in the lathe.
When this has taken out all
file marks, clean the polisher

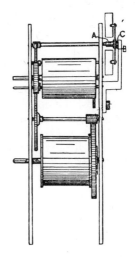

Fig. 88.—Arrangement
Chiming Train.

thoroughly, refile it, and charge again with "red-stuff" and
oil, which will bring up a good polish in a few minutes,
especially if the speed is fairly high. The polisher and the
red-stuff should be kept quite clean and covered up
from dust.

Main Wheel.—The main wheel must be turned true in
the centre, as must all the wheels, before opening it out
with a broach to fit the arbor of the barrel. It is important
that it should fit without shake. It is necessary that the
centres of all the wheels should be turned true, because
when the wheels are cut they are only approximately
true to their centres; consequently there is no guarantee
that the centre hole is the true centre of the circle of teeth.
The centres of all the wheels may as well be turned true
at once in the same chuck to save time and trouble. To do
this, mount a piece of wood on the face-plate of the lathe,
and face it true and flat. Then with a sharp chisel and at

high speed make in it a shallow depression, into which the smallest wheel can be just pushed friction tight to the bottom. The wheel thus held by the points of the teeth must run quite truly. While thus held turn out the centre hole true, after which it can be opened out by means of broaches for fitting; then enlarge the depression in the wood for the next wheel, and so on until all are done. The fitting and fastening on of the main wheel to the barrel and the making of the "click" and its spring can all be copied directly from the other barrels.

Pinions.—Pinion turning will not be found so easy an operation as barrel turning; but with a fine pair of female turning-centres, and a running centre which is perfectly true, it can be accomplished in any ordinary small lathe. It is quite impossible to turn pinions between ordinary or male centres. Start on the pinion for the 80 wheel, as that is the stoutest. Cut off the required length, and centre it to run quite truly. The centres will have to be filed up. When centred it will present the appearance shown in Fig. 28. Turn two nicks, marking out the portion of the leaves it is desired to leave on, and, removing it from the lathe, proceed to file off the useless part of the leaves, and leave only the centre core. Then turn the pinion true throughout, and it is ready for hardening and tempering.

To harden the pinion, heat it to a full and even red from end to end, and plunge it end-on into cold water and stir it round; or the water may be stirred up and the pinion plunged in and held quite still. Brighten with emery-cloth, and very carefully reheat over a clean flame, like a Bunsen burner or a spirit lamp, until the pinion takes a deep blue colour from end to end, after which the centre portion may be let down still more to a pale blue. This will facilitate straightening should it happen to have gone out of truth in the hardening. Place the pinion in the lathe again and test for truth; bend it until the pinion portion runs quite truly; the other part does not matter, as it can be reduced until true by turning. It can then be turned and pivoted, and the pivots polished as before described.

Wheel Mounting.—The 80 wheel is mounted on a brass collet. To make this, drill up a piece of brass rod in the lathe, and roughly turn it to shape; then solder it on to the pinion and turn true, taking great care with the seating for the wheel. Rivet the wheel on well with a punch, having previously notched the hole in the wheel to prevent turning round. A wheel mounted thus should go on quite truly. The pinion for the 63 wheel must have a rather large front pivot, and come through the front plate in the same manner as the corresponding wheel of the striking train.

Other Pinions.—The warning-wheel pinion needs no special directions, except that, as it is slender, only its ends need be hardened. The same remark applies to the fly pinion, which, it will be seen from Fig. 88, extends through the back plate and is carried by a large brass cock.

Fly.—The "fly" is of the regulating pattern, as shown in Fig. 88. It consists of two square canes, $\frac{1}{2}$ in. by $\frac{1}{2}$ in., or $\frac{3}{8}$ in. by $\frac{3}{4}$ in., supported on a cross-arm riveted to a central "pipe" turning loosely on the pinion. It is held friction tight by being kept pressed down to a thin curved brass spring with a central hole in it, which passes over the pinion and rests against a shoulder. The fly is held up to this spring by means of a pin through the pinion.

Chime-barrel Arbor.—The chime-barrel arbor is made of a piece of steel rod about $\frac{3}{16}$ in. thick, turned up true and pivoted and polished like the rest. Before proceeding with this, it will be necessary to decide whether single four-bell or eight-bell chimes are wanted, or both; because if both are wanted and a changing mechanism, the arbor will need to have an "end-shake" between the plates, or a "pump action" of $\frac{1}{8}$ in. to allow of the change of chimes. In Fig. 88 this is shown to be the case. Having turned the arbor, mount the 40 wheel on it so that it will gear properly with the 80 wheel in both positions of the arbor, allowing for the shifting. The chime barrel is made from the brass tube already specified. First drive on and solder brass discs to form the ends; turn them true and then solder on the tube, afterwards turning that true all over. Make it the whole available length of the arbor. The complete chime train can then be pitched between the plates, as shown in Figs. 87 and 88.

Pitching the Depths.—To pitch the depths correctly, the wheels and pinions must be carefully measured with fine-pointed compasses, and then transferred to the plates. To do this, the theory of "depths" must, to a certain extent, be understood. If the teeth of the main wheel are examined, they will be seen to consist of straight radial lines up to a certain spot called the "pitch circle", beyond which they are curved to a point. These curved portions are the parts that act on the pinion leaves. If a pinion is examined, the leaves will be found likewise to consist of radial straight lines up to the "pitch circle", beyond which they are rounded by a semicircle. It is the *straight* portions on which the curved points of the wheel teeth act; therefore, if the pinions turned from the pinion wire are not well shaped, file out the leaves deep and straight, and smooth them up carefully with emery on wood.

For a depth to run perfectly the pitch circles must roll on one another, as in Fig. 27, which shows a portion of a wheel and pinion, the "pitch circles" being drawn. Therefore to pitch a depth, the actual diameters of the wheels and pinions are not considered, but the diameters of the pitch circles only. To pitch, for example, the main wheel depth with the 80-wheel pinion, first drill the barrel arbor pivot-holes in the correct position level with the centre-wheel hole and the striking barrel. Then with fine compasses measure the full diameter of the pitch circle of the main wheel, and transfer it to a line drawn on a sheet of smooth white paper. Next measure the diameter of the pitch circle of the 80-wheel pinion, and add it to the other on the same straight line. Then, by trial with the compasses, find the exact half of the length, and transfer it to the plate as the required distance between the barrel pivot-holes and the 80-wheel pivot-holes to form a correct depth. Pitch all the depths in this way, and drill the pivot-holes in the plate, transferring them to the other plate by pinning the plates together and marking through as before.

Bells, Hammers, etc.—The set of eight chime bells, forming a complete octave, is mounted on a spindle, supported by two uprights screwed to the back and front plates respectively. Small wooden washers, $\frac{1}{8}$ in. apart, are placed between each bell and its neighbour so as to separate them, the eight bells thus ranging over $1\frac{7}{8}$ in.; if the pillars are only 2 in. long the bells must be spaced more closely. The eight hammers work in slots cut in a brass block screwed across the top corner of the frame in recesses cut for it, as shown in Fig. 90. It should be about $\frac{3}{4}$ in. wide, $\frac{3}{8}$ in. deep, and the length equal to the width of the frame.

The hammers are made of flat steel or iron, rather thin, say a little less than $\frac{1}{16}$ in. thick. They all work on one pin running from end to end of the brass block. To drill a hole for a small pin from end to end through a $2\frac{1}{2}$-in. brass block would be no easy job, so it is managed in this way. The brass block, on the under-side, is cut halfway through with a saw from end to end (a tenon saw cuts brass well). A slip of brass to fill up the saw-cut, all but a small space for the wire, is then filed up and soldered in and filed off flush outside, as shown in Fig. 89. The pin should project at the ends to facilitate removal.

The hammer heads are of brass, and are driven or screwed on. The hammer springs are made from a thin piece of brass, and are like a comb with eight teeth, the whole being fixed to a support, as shown in Figs. 87 and 90. The hammer stems should be bent to suit the bells, that which is to strike the smallest bell being farther forward than that which is to strike the largest bell. But the tails, which should just clear the chime barrel, must all be in a straight line. The slots in which they work should

L

Fig. 89.— End-view
of Hammer Lock.

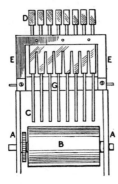

Fig. 90.—Plate with
Hammer Springs.

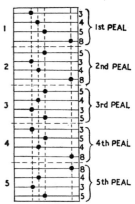

Fig. 91.—Positions of
Pins for Westminster
Chimes.

be cut to such a depth as to ensure this, or stops can be
arranged for each hammer if desired. The following are the
letter references in Fig. 90: A the plates, B the chime barrel,
C the hammer tails, D the hammer heads, E the frame for
the hammer springs, F the hammer-spring "comb", and
G the hammer rack.

Motion Work.—Very precise directions cannot be given
as to the rest of the mechanism, as so much depends on
the size and arrangement of the movement in hand;
therefore a description of the action of the motion work
will now be given, which should enable the worker to
complete it correctly.

As the clock approaches a quarter, one of the four pins
marked on the minute wheel E in Fig. 87 advances and
begins to raise the lever H. This also raises J (in one piece

with it) and the quarter rack hook G. The quarter rack F then falls until its tail rests on the snail E (with four steps). The rack, in falling, releases the gathering pallet and the chiming train "warns", being stopped by the pin in the warning wheel coming in contact with the steel block in the warning lever. The train is thus held stationary until, as the minute wheel E advances, the pin finally passes the warning lever H, and the latter falls, at the same time releasing the pin in the warning wheel and allowing the rack hook G to fall, and the clock chimes the quarter. That is to say, supposing the rack F fell on the first step of the snail E, it would fall a distance equal to one tooth. Therefore, the gathering pallet would make one revolution and gather up the one tooth, coming again to rest on the pin in the rack. One revolution of the pallet wheel being equal to one-fifth of a revolution of the chiming drum, the latter would move one-fifth of a turn and chime one "peal", or one quarter, it being spaced into five divisions, each having one "peal" pinned on it.

There are thus five "peals". No. 1 is struck at fifteen minutes; Nos. 2 and 3 are struck at thirty minutes; Nos. 4, 5, and 1 at forty-five minutes; and Nos. 2, 3, 4, and 5 at the hour. The chime barrel thus makes two revolutions for each hour, chiming ten peals, one at the first quarter, two at the half-hour, three at the three-quarter hour, and four at the hour.

During all this time the striking train is locked by the gathering pallet being in contact with the pin in the hour rack B (Fig. 87). The pin I in the quarter rack goes right through and projects on both sides. The front portion locks the quarter gathering pallet, and the back portion engages with the tail end of the hour warning lever, and when the rack is all gathered up, pulls this tail up, leaving the striking train free to run as far as the pin in the warning wheel is concerned. It, however, cannot run because it is locked by its gathering pallet. When the quarter rack falls, the hour warning lever rises, its tail end being released, and is in a position to intercept the pin in the hour warning wheel.

At fifteen minutes the quarter rack falls on the first step of the quarter snail E, and one "peal" is chimed, warning lever D being meanwhile released and pulled down again, effecting nothing, the striking train being locked by its gathering pallet.

At thirty minutes the quarter rack falls on the second step of the quarter snail, and two "peals" are chimed, the same process being repeated as regards the hour warning lever.

At forty-five minutes three "peals" are chimed, with the same action as before.

At the hour the quarter rack falls on the fourth and deepest step of the quarter snail, and the rack falls four teeth, the pin I coming in contact with the tail of the hour-rack hook C, which it raises, letting the hour rack B fall. The hour gathering pallet is then released, and the hour striking train runs and "warns" until the pin in the warning wheel comes in contact with the steel projection in the hour warning lever D, which has been allowed to rise on the falling of the quarter rack F. When the hour is reached, the quarter warning lever H falls, the quarter rack is gathered up, and four peals are chimed. As the last tooth is finally gathered up, the pin I in the quarter rack pulls up the tail of the hour warning lever D and releases the hour striking train, which then runs and strikes the hour until its gathering pallet is stopped by coming again in contact with the pin in the hour rack.

The reader is advised to study this action very carefully, for until it is thoroughly understood the mechanism cannot possibly be correctly made. The rules for putting striking clocks together must be observed throughout, namely, when the trains are "locked" by the gathering pallets, the hour hammer and quarter hammers respectively must be quite free of their lifting pins, and not the least bit "on the rise". Also, the pins in the warning wheels must have at least half a turn of run to their stop pieces.

Placing Pins in Chime Barrel.—The placing of the pins in the chime drum or barrel can now be described. As before explained, there are five "peals" equally spaced out on the barrel, the barrel moving one-fifth of a revolution for each tooth of the quarter-rack gathered up. For con· venience, the smallest bell will be called No. 1, and so on to the largest, No. 8. For eight-bell chimes (sometimes erroneously called Cambridge chimes, though, as a matter of fact, Cambridge and Westminster chimes are identical), the eight bells are all used, pretty much in any order the maker may desire; a selection may be made from the following very usual ones, or any others may be devised, five, of course, being chosen.

(1)   1, 2, 3, 4, 5, 6, 7, 8.
(2)   1, 3, 5, 7, 2, 4, 6, 8.
(3)   4, 3, 2, 1, 5, 2, 7, 8.
(4)   1, 4, 3, 6, 5, 7, 2, 8.
(5)   4, 6, 5, 3, 7, 6, 1, 8.

On the other hand, the Westminster chimes are invariable, and are struck on four only of the eight bells. So that if Westminster chimes alone are wanted, the set of bells should consist of four; but for eight-bell chimes, or eight and four bells with a changing mechanism, the whole eight are used, the Westminster chimes being taken on Nos. 3, 4, 5, and 8. The arrangement is as follows:

(1)   3, 4, 5, 8.
(2)   5, 3, 4, 8.
(3)   5, 4, 3, 5.
(4)   3, 5, 4, 8.
(5)   8, 4, 3, 5.

The first thing to do is accurately to divide the barrel

into five sections by straight lines from end to end. This can conveniently be done by means of the wheel of 40 teeth mounted on it. Each portion is then marked off as shown in Fig. 91, which represents the five peals with the positions of the pins marked for Westminster chimes. As shown in the figure, there is a slight pause between each peal. The circles on which the pin-holes are drilled are accurately marked beneath each hammer tail and run round in the lathe. The cross lines must be drawn at equal intervals, or the chiming will be jerky and irregular.

If a change of chimes is desired, these circles for the pin-holes must be marked with the barrel at one extreme position, and the barrel afterwards shifted to the other extreme, and eight more circles made for the eight-bell chimes. In this case, eight transverse lines must be made in each section, and the positions of pins carefully plotted out, according to the chimes chosen. Against the back plate a flat brass spring is fixed, which always keeps the chime barrel forward against the front pivot shoulder and on one set of chimes. To change it a lever is set, turning on a stud screwed into the front plate; the end is bevelled where it presses on the front pivot of the chime barrel, and so depresses it. The upper end of the lever is made accessible to the hand by a small slot cut in the edge of the dial near the top, out of sight.

CHAPTER 18

Pendulums

CALCULATING Length.—A pendulum that is approximately 39 in. long takes one second to complete a single swing. From this can be calculated the length of any pendulum if the number of vibrations or beats per minute is known, as explained below, always remembering that the time occupied by a pendulum in making a swing varies as the square of the length. Thus a two seconds pendulum is four times the length of a one-second pendulum.

To find the length of a pendulum for any given clock, first find the number of vibrations it is required to make in one minute, and then find the length of a pendulum making that number either from a table of lengths or by calculation. To find the required number of vibrations per minute, multiply together the numbers of the teeth in the centre wheel, third wheel, and 'scape wheel. Divide this by the numbers of the third pinion and 'scape pinion and 30 multiplied together. Thus, suppose the centre wheel is 64, third wheel 60, pinion 8, 'scape wheel 30, pinion 8, then $\frac{64 \times 60 \times 30}{8 \times 8 \times 30} = 60 =$ number of vibrations per minute.

To find the length of the pendulum making this number of vibrations per minute, divide 375·4 by the number and square the result. Thus $\frac{375·4}{60} = 6·26$; this squared $= 39·18$, which is approximately the length of the seconds pendulum in England. Or, make a proportion sum, calculating from the length of the seconds pendulum, 39 in. (about). Thus (Required number of beats)^2 : 60^2 :: 39 in. : required length. If 120 be the number of beats, then 120^2 : 60^2 ::

39 in. : required length; which, being computed, equals 14,400 : 3,600 :: 39 in. : 9¾ in.

A variation of the above method of ascertaining the number of beats per minute is to count the train wheels, multiply together the numbers of the centre wheels, third, and escape wheels, and double the result. Divide this successively by the third and escape pinions, and the result is the number of beats in one hour. Divide this by 60 and it will give the number per minute. For example, centre 84, third 73, escape 32, and pinions of 7. 84 × 78 × 32 × 2 = 419,328. This divided by 7 twice = 8,558 = number of beats per hour; 8,558 ÷ 60 = 142 = number of beats per minute. Then from a table of pendulum lengths it can be seen that a pendulum to give this number of beats per minute must be 6·9 in. long, or nearly 7 in. This measurement is from the top of the suspension spring (where it bends) to centre of bob. A little extra length should always be allowed for regulating.

Grandfather clocks and clocks which beat true seconds have pendulums approximately 39 in. long. Those Vienna regulator clocks that beat three times in two seconds have pendulums 18 in. long. Half-second pendulums, as in some English dials and some American clocks, measure 10 in.; quarter-second pendulums, as in "tictacs", 2½ in. But pendulums of all conceivable lengths between these are frequently used.

Weights of Pendulum Bobs.—There is no rule as to the weight of a clock pendulum, but it should be said that the best clocks carry the heaviest pendulums. Weight does not effect the time of vibration; that depends solely on the length. The weights of pendulum bobs vary from 2 lb. to 5 lb. in grandfather clocks; they may be in the neighbourhood of 2 lb. in English dials and as little as 1 oz. or even less in small American and Continental clocks.

Wooden Seconds Pendulum.—For a seconds pendulum having a bob resting on a rating nut, the first consideration is to secure a piece of perfectly straight-grained, well-seasoned wood. A second-hand furniture or marine-store dealer's is a likely source. Wood rods are varnished, polished, or painted to repel the effect of atmospheric changes. The suspension spring is fitted in a slot cut in a brass cap fitted over the top of the rod, and fixed with two pins. A piece of thin brass tube is fitted on the end to receive the rating nut. A thin brass casing is fixed for the crutch engagement. Mahogany, ebony, and other woods are often employed for shorter pendulums, because deal would be unsound for the attachments in small sizes. The bob should be of lead, cased in brass if thought necessary for the sake of appearance.

Compensation Pendulums.—Clocks, like watches, have their rates affected by changes in the temperature. A rise in the temperature is accompanied by a lengthening of the pendulum rod, and the clock accordingly loses, just in the same manner as it would if the bob had been lowered by means of the regulating screw. The reverse of this occurs when the temperature falls.

The lengthening of the pendulum rod being the main cause of the loss through heat, it is evident that if a material could be found, and used in its construction, that did not expand under the action of heat, there would be no temperature error worth considering. A near approach to these conditions is found in a pendulum composed of a piece of thoroughly seasoned wood and a heavy round bob of no great height. Such pendulums are nearly always found in church clocks of the common kind, and also in some regulators, and the results are very satisfactory.

Clocks fitted with these pendulums do lose a little on being subjected to heat, and gain in the cold. It has there-fore been suggested to compensate the remaining error by fitting the plain wood rod with a lead bob in the shape of a thick tube about one-quarter or one-third of the length of the pendulum, and resting at its lower end on the regulating screw. This has been found an improvement, and in this form it can lay some claim to be termed a true compensation pendulum. The theory of the arrangement is as follows: On heating, the wood rod expands and lengthens a trifle; the lead bob also lengthens, and lead expanding more under the influence of heat than wood, its centre of gravity is raised, it being supported by its under edge. This brings back the centre of oscillation of the pendulum to where it was before, or very nearly so.

If the expansion of wood were quite regular and could always be depended upon to be the same, this kind of pendulum would give a true compensation; but it does not and for the best results other kinds of pendulums are used.

Among these, the mercurial form is perhaps the most accurate—at all events, it is the most popular. Fig. 92 shows a mercurial pendulum of the ordinary form. The rod is of steel, and the bob consists of a glass jar filled with mercury. It acts as follows: Mercury expands under the influence of heat about sixteen times as much as steel. The effect of heat on the rod is to lengthen it, and lower the glass jar of mercury. The effect on the mercury is to expand and rise in the jar. If the quantity of mercury is properly proportioned to the length of the steel rod, an exact compensation is arrived at. The foregoing is theory. In practice, it is found that under a sudden change of temperature the thin steel rod is affected more quickly than the jar of mercury, and, as it were, the rod gets a start of the mercury and causes an error, which occurs at each change of temperature.

To avoid this there was invented a form of mercury pendulum in which the rod is a steel tube and the mercury is inside it. This ensures their being of the same temperature.

The next form of compensation is the "zinc and steel", shown in Figs. 93 and 94. It consists of a steel rod A, over which there is a zinc tube B fastened to the rod A at its lower end only. Depending from the zinc tube B is an iron or steel tube C, to the lower end of which the bob D is fixed. It will thus be seen that any lengthening of the steel rod or tube tends to lower the bob, while a lengthening of the zinc tube B raises it. Remembering that zinc expands more than twice as much as steel, the one length of zinc tube just counteracts the two lengths of steel, and a compensation is effected.

One other form of compensation pendulum is the "gridiron", which was one of the earliest made. But for its ungainly appearance it would, perhaps, have been much more widely used than it is. It consists of a central steel rod and a set of vertical bars of brass and steel side by side, so arranged that while the expansion of the steel rods lowers the bob, that of the brass rods raises it. Brass expands more than steel, and therefore by making the total lengths of the brass rods and steel rods in inverse proportion to their rates of expansion, a compensation is effected. (Fig. 67.)

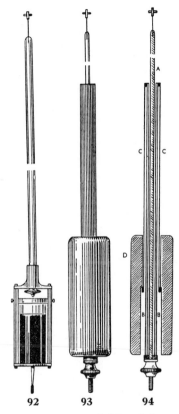

92   93   94

Fig. 92.—Mercurial Pendulum.
Fig. 93.—Zinc and Steel Pendulum.
Fig. 94.—Section through Zinc and Steel Pendulum.

However, the introduction of a special alloy for pendulum manufacture has more or less relegated the above types of pendulum to the past.

Invar.—This is a nickel-steel alloy compounded by Dr. C. E. Guillaume, of the International Weights and Measures Office at Sèvres, near Paris. Its special property is an extremely small coefficient of expansion; that is to say, it expands or contracts only very slightly on being subjected to changes of temperature. All metals expand in length and breadth when heated, and contract when cooled. Thus a brass rod will expand in length to an extent equal to ·002 of its length when heated from the freezing point to the boiling point of water; while a steel rod under the same conditions will not expand so much, the exact extent being ·0011, or a little more than half the expansion of the brass; but a rod of first-grade invar will expand only ·00008, or about one-fourteenth the expansion of steel. Thus a clock having a pendulum rod of invar has hardly any temperature error at all, the amount being quite inappreciable in ordinary clocks, and only becoming apparent in high-class regulators.

The following calculation shows still more clearly the relative expansions of these three metals, the figures indicating the expansion per mile for an increase of 1° C.: First-grade invar, $\frac{1}{20}$ or ·05 ins.; second-grade invar, $\frac{2}{20}$ or ·1 in.; third-grade invar, $\frac{3}{20}$ or ·15 in.; steel, $\frac{14}{20}$ or ·7 in.; brass, $1\frac{5}{20}$ or 1·25 in. Thus a brass wire which measures one mile in length at 20° C. will increase in length by $1\frac{1}{4}$ in. if warmed up to 21° C.; while an invar wire under the same conditions will measure only $\frac{1}{20}$ in. more.

It will be noticed that three grades of invar are mentioned, having different expansion values. The first grade expands least, and is the most costly; the second and third grades expand a little more, but are much cheaper. The metal is procurable in the form of sheet, wire, or rod. For clock-makers, pendulum rod lengths of 3 ft. 9 in. each are specially made.

Invar was tested carefully, both at Sèvres and at Kew Observatory, and the trials confirm the inventor's claims, thus placing the accuracy of the figures beyond dispute.

In face of these facts, it would be folly to make compensation pendulums of any other metal. The necessity for mercurial and zinc-and-steel compensation pendulums no longer exists. Taking first the third-grade invar—the cheapest—an almost perfect compensation will be attained by threading its lower end to take a rating nut and using a lead cylindrical bob 8 in. high, resting on the rating nut, the upward expansion of 8 in. of lead compensating for the downward expansion of the inner rod. With second-grade invar, a cast-iron cylindrical bob 1 ft. 1 in. high resting on the rating nut, or a 7-in. high lead bob would be necessary. Using first-grade invar and a 15-lb. cast-iron bob 6½ in high, an almost perfect pendulum will be obtained.

Any of these pendulums can be adjusted, if found under- or over-compensated, by varying the height of the bob a trifle. They are all seconds pendulums measuring 3 ft. 3¼ in. from the point of suspension to the centre of the bob. For ordinary house clocks with short pendulums, the third-grade invar pendulum rod may be cut up and brass bobs fitted having a height equal to a quarter the length of the pendulum rod. Thus for an 8-in. pendulum the rod will have to be 9⅛ in. long from the point of suspension to the bottom of the bob, and the brass bob 2¼ in. high. This will give a pendulum of 8 in. acting length.

INDEX